THE MOUNTAIN ARABS

ALSO BY JOHN SYKES

The Levantine
The Romantic Wife
The Newcomer
The Ocean Crossing
A Japanese Family
The Quakers
The Colonial
Family in Peru
The Heat of Summer
Caique
The Couple
Direction North

THE MOUNTAIN ARABS

A WINDOW ON THE MIDDLE EAST

by John Sykes

CHILTON BOOK COMPANY

Philadelphia   New York   London

TO JOHN AND JOSEY

Ahlan wa sahlan

Contents

1

THE NIGHT BEFORE
THE WAR BROKE OUT
(June 4, 1967)

1

THE NIGHT BEFORE
THE WAR BROKE OUT
(June 4, 1967)

ALL morning people from the village had been calling at the house. They knew that Sheik Nassib had not come, but Leila and, for all his manner, Raoul were also members of the dominant clan, therefore, intermediaries to be consulted. Salutations hummed on the air. To the left of the courtyard the long room with its high, triple-arched windows and loose-covered settees had been filling gradually and had begun to sound like an interminable music-box. A few men just up from the city, though born nearby and still voting here, in some cases accompanied by their wives, stayed for the formal coffee then escaped from Raoul's smiling malevolence. But the villagers themselves, the mountain people, sat and sat and softly gave their views in turn to each newcomer, and in the pause of listening called on God, then continued as before—hoping no doubt that the Sheik would come, their Deputy to whom, despite the crisis, they could each slip in a personal need, though as a body now it was his leadership they sought. Meanwhile, waiting and keeping abreast of each nuance of the village mood, the villagers were also listening to the ominous sounds about the house—the women busy on the upper floor opening up the place for occupation. If the Sheik himself, a month

3

earlier than usual, was moving his establishment up to the mountains, then the most pessimistic views were justified. What did Monsieur Raoul think?

Raoul was a master of evasion. He had never been known to give a straight reply. He delighted in the most tortuous argument, barbed to scandalize his listeners and, where he could chance it, to make them squirm. His smile, his elegant phrasing, and his reputation as a prominent Lebanese poet permitted him to get away with much. Raoul abhorred, I knew, the current Middle East crisis. He disliked, for different reasons, each contestant. He shared none of the Arab exultation, or, in Christian circles, their fears. He was convinced, it seemed, of coming war and defeat and thought the whole affair had been engineered by Russia to strengthen her grip on Egypt. He saw only slow decline for the area into a semi-industrialized slum.

These were not views to voice at the moment. Today, however, he was likely to be careful. He had been given a special assignment by the Sheik at a village higher up the mountain. It was so important, he had confided in his cryptic way, "that it even mattered what I ate for breakfast." He was not to expend himself en route. We were only staying a few hours at the house so Leila could check on the maids. She too was holding court in some other room at the back, appearing from time to time in Raoul's room, increasingly full-faced and flushed, to make sure his guests were served. Her appearance soothed him also, curbing any waspishness, for the one person he unreservedly loved was his sister Leila. His smile for her was playful, contrite, at moments unashamedly spiritual.

He managed thus to answer the villagers by saying next to nothing at all, that is, he said, when addressed in French, that if only America could eventually mature (Did he mean in the next twenty-four hours?), then problems might find easier solutions.

I could not follow what they said in Arabic.

The view from the courtyard, from beside the fountain with a covered alcove, or *liwan*, at the back, was of the two stone-built wings of the house, each with its delicate tracery of windows, and beyond, the vertiginous drop to the sea. I believe the altitude was three-thousand feet. Some miles away, the sea glittered in metallic haze. Immediately below was a natural escarpment, then spurs of rock still holding pines, then alternating scrub and scree, crags, precipices falling rapidly, at clear hours to the narrow plain, but on this humid morning to a veil of steam obliterating all beneath. Beirut had disappeared. One did not have to lament that, but just to the north where, most improbably (for the drop to the coast was almost as sudden), a stairway of terraces had been constructed down from a projecting spine of the range, these too, and the satisfaction that merely to observe them always gave, were being engulfed by the rising mist, billowing up toward our aerie.

Up here the air was a singing blue, each object standing clear.

I had been trying for the hundredth time in Lebanon to read the account of an earlier traveler. Volney, Bell, Burton, Lamartine, de Nerval, Charles H. Churchill, and others, were waiting in a Beirut apartment for the borrowing. I was beginning to feel that I should never read them. Conversation always intervened. One's Arab friends, once contact was established, remorselessly took over one's time.

As now, what with the dizzy view and the airy splash of the fountain in the sunlight, and with brooding on the snatches of talk overheard and indeed on the tragedy about to be enacted, I had no more than skimmed another chapter when

Raoul shot out: "They have mostly left. You come and say your word on Nasser."

His wry, barbed smile was a warning to be cautious. Only a French-speaking doctor, a storekeeper, and a muleteer remained. They were all Maronites; good Catholic Lebanese. The muleteer had sat there longest but looked least exhausted by discussion. In any case, the doctor had the floor, explaining, during the exchange of courtesies, that his summer villa was on the road above and that he was an old friend of Sheik Nassib. In his hand he held a long-stemmed rose, which he immediately offered me as a gift.

His view was: "There will be no war. Israel has missed its chance to give battle. This morning the news is that thousands of Israelis have returned to the beaches round Tel Aviv. So Nasser has won. What a fantastic bluff! Look at his reputation last month, and look where he stands again today! He is the Captain again of the Muslim world, the new Salah al-Din (Saladin) as they call him. I tell you, as an Arab I am proud of this achievement. We have regained territory; we have withstood America. I thought that he was overreaching himself, but no one matches Nasser at bluffing. He will cripple Israel economically and make her sue to the Palestinians. I tell you, as an Arab I acclaim Nasser! He is smart, *shâtir*. We used to say, a thousand ladders cannot reach his head, but as you say in England, laugh last, laugh loudest! Yes, God be praised. But as a Christian Lebanese"— his broad, slack face slackened further—"I am not so happy. It affects our position."

He began to suck his teeth, discretion clamping onto his surge of jubilation. He stared out of the window, suddenly indifferent.

The storekeeper added to the praise of Nasser, noting how he had played the Russians. The muleteer sat benignly puzzled.

All morning this had been the chorus. Old history, as well as the preamble to this latest mood, had been retold. Nasser, in closing the Straits of Tiran, had released joy in the Arab world. Years of frustration, of acutely feeling the humiliation of the refugees, had been turned to a shining sword of decision. A war of liberation had been launched.

Then fear had entered in. The Great Powers had interests that might touch off a planetary conflict. People had stared into the abyss. They had begun loudly to berate America and warn her not to challenge the Arabs who were set upon their course of justice. Who had first supported the Zionists? England had been berated too. Those twin Powers had been warned to stay neutral, or else the shining Arabian sword would swiftly fall upon their necks. Russia, China, U Thant, De Gaulle—these names, through the morning's recital, had stood up to be counted as allies. The note of fear had been forgotten.

Justifiably so, for a crushing victory had been attained without recourse to fighting. Nasser, Nasser! He had ringed Israel with steel. Nasser, Nasser! He had united their race, bringing Arabs from the Maghreb shoulder to shoulder with Arabs from the Euphrates. The brotherly kiss for Hussein was symbolic. It was good to feel Arab, with their world on the move. Something of an old spirit was trumpeting.

Then silences had intervened, incalculable with contrary feelings. They were Christians, Maronites, the suspect minority within this dominant sphere of Islam. They were Arabs also, but their case was different. Lebanon itself was a compromise.

Silences, but eloquence was pleasant, and today wise men praised Nasser. Tomorrow was soon enough for anxieties, and the Sheik meanwhile would give them a lead.

Though why, by the by, in this hour of victory was the

Sheik moving his family up to the mountains? Had he information that the Beirut mob in the name of Nasser would next turn on the Christians?

More silence. Like the silence, the doctor, with another exchange of courtesies, then the storekeeper, and then, hesitantly, the muleteer, departed from the house.

"What did the muleteer mutter while leaving?"

"A mountain phrase. It more or less means: 'Look where the shadows are concealing Druzes.' He still obviously thinks there will be trouble."

"Do you still think there will be war?"

"Who now can turn off the steam? Don't you imagine the Israelis will profit from this opportunity? Those pathetic Egyptians! It will be a massacre."

Raoul and Leila had been born in Egypt and until 1956 had lived there, the children of a high government official, Abdallah Hadiri, who had been dismissed by Nasser because he was Lebanese and who had died afterward. It had left hard feelings. They had lost much wealth. Raoul was mordant on the subject of the United Arab Republic. But equally, he had loved the country, Cairo, the Delta, the desert wadis, and perhaps a part of his tenderness for Leila came from their having, together, been thrown out of that childhood paradise. His recent poetry suggested this.

He disliked talking politics for long, and he had really suffered, and with meekness, that morning! One could not associate meekness with Raoul. He was undertaking this for the Sheik. The least one could do was to find another topic. But now, as I had experienced on other occasions, despite his wide range of interests, and scholarship, and verbal fluency, conversation with Raoul was impossible unless he was riding his own compulsions. He would not respond. He gave weak replies. He had thrown an impenetrable wall about himself, until, suddenly, he was hammering you again with a black joke or a prejudice, or some dry remark on his family. For the Hadiri clan he was the odd man out but he was their poet, and so forgiven.

He had nothing to say. He looked numbed, as disconnected as the white mist rising toward us. Then Leila swept out, with a maid in tow, bringing beer and lunch to the courtyard.

We had been promised a picnic, a few sandwiches; the women would be too busy to do more. Needless to say, it was an intricate feast.

Leila presided, palpitating happily.

Lunch over, we continued the climb.

No sooner out on the road again when noise and confusion slammed about us. There was an upward sweep of cars from the city, thrusting from one steep bend to the next. The only rule was "Get ahead!" The connecting straight bits were used as springboards for the challenge of the corners when two or sometimes three came abreast where there was only place for one. Nerve counted, and, of course, good luck. If at that moment a car were descending, as likely as not there would be a crash. Crashes were two for a penny in Lebanon. The roadsides were littered with burnt-out wrecks or cars upturned at the foot of precipices. Smashed fenders, bent bumpers, were small change. There seemed to be a need for the more dramatic write-off. It was the pace of a growing middle-class affluence bursting out of the overcrowded city and flaunting itself, especially on Sundays, with extreme self-interest and arrogance wrapped up in an all-excusing fatalism that counted nothing, not even death, to be a hazard worth applying the brakes for.

The Lebanese roads were a hard school.

Raoul, at the wheel of a Ford Cortina, had pushed, as was standard local practice, out of the driveway without a pause into the thick flow of traffic. We were part of the melee, though not too active, because Leila's heart, she said, could not stand it. We were being overtaken continuously; edged continuously into the ditch. A service-taxi, one of the sort that accommodates up to five passengers and keeps to a route like any bus, kept stopping to discharge a passenger or replace him, then again came rocketing past us, tooting, the driver with one hand outside—for the air, or was it from sheer bravado, or to wave to an acquaintance here or there—while the other hand simultaneously steered, flicked the gears through, took money from a passenger, and held a large sandwich to his mouth. He drove his taxi like a hot rodder; curving away from oncoming vehicles; gathering speed till nothing could stop him from swinging out around a blind corner. Round he went with screeching tires. And there he was again, honor satisfied, finally folding into the queue. A very large bus was descending. But what if they had met on the corner?

Raoul took this behavior for granted, and the music of horns and police whistles—protesting, acclaiming, who could say?—and the sudden rush of the precipice toward us, or the stone ramparts of buildings above. He shrugged at Leila's exclamations. He pointed to the splendid views of Sannin; the snow-clad peak that crowned the range here. He said that at Easter, when he had been up skiing, all these heights had been snow-covered, and they were only an hour from the sea and a quick spring dip, though the winter had been so prolonged this year that wolves had been reported again. He said: "Look, now you see the mountains! You see why it's a world to itself. From Beirut and the coast one gets the picture of a single, overtowering wall simply there to keep out the desert. Now, at this level, you see how, in fact, there is a complex pattern of cross-rifting, with high, fertile plateaus between. A good place to hide away in, eh? It always has been. A refuge for minorities, in particular for the Maronite Christian community. Without this they would not have survived. There would have been no independent Lebanon."

He grinned, "I suppose Hamid keeps saying how conceited we Maronites are?"

"You know him better than I."

"He is absolutely right. Yet we do bring a special flavor into this corner of the Arab world. And it begins here, in these mountain recesses, where our ancestors kept their freedom."

Geographically there was a simple explanation. The highest strata of the range, which within Lebanon ran almost the length of the country, were of limestone, and thus they were eroded by rainfall into a series of high ridges with deep gorges and prolonged cliff faces falling away to the next level. Here the rock was sandstone, with marls and lignite, and so more resistant to erosion. It gave for the next two-thousand feet, from five down to three-thousand feet, a pattern of gently spring-watered slopes, suited in that wonderful air and sunshine to fruit-growing, to olives, and wheat. Where among the higher crags and cols there were only pine and juniper and fir and a profusion, in spring, of alpine flowers, at this more domestic level there were oaks, and maple, cypress, walnut, fig, carob, even a few cedars. There were orchards sloping or neatly terraced, vineyards, and again terraces of wheat descending to the verge of the next steep drop. The third stratum, down to the coast, was again of limestone and so indented, splintered most complexly, with precipitous ravines. If one saw it from out at sea, it gave the illusion of a sheer crag face on which, miraculously, roads and villas by the thousand had been constructed. A wall, as Raoul now aptly put it, against the vast inland desert.

It would have been some climb for invading armies and for city tax collectors. Hardly worth it, prior to the last century, if a token arrangement could be made with chieftains. Therein lay, as Raoul said, one basic factor permitting the Maronites and other Christian groups and Muslim dissenters (such as the Druzes and Shia communities), fleeing from the Sunni governors of the plains, to maintain their individual character. Therein, as he said, lay the story of Lebanon.

We were still approximately at three-thousand feet. For though we had climbed a few steep bends, we had coasted down along a broad ridge dotted with a succession of villages. These all looked fairly well-to-do, not so much nowadays from mountain farming as from remittances flowing home from emigrants in the Americas, Australia, and Africa, money, put into solid housing or even, incongruously in that rural area, into blocks of apartments that in turn were rented to the money-bringing summer visitors. It was the new economy overtaking the old, leaving runs of terraces in poor repair. Villagers, too, were moving down to Beirut and to the new coastal zones for industry. But some of them, working in the city, also drove up and down each day or took advantage of the fast service-taxis. On a Sunday like this they were in the village cafés, shirt-sleeved, playing backgammon. Cars were wedged on either side of the road. Balconies, flights of steps, terraces were thick with children in clean, bright clothes. The women, except for the richer town girls who flashed up in sports cars, were more discreetly out of sight, or in attendance on their children, or walking together in twos and threes for a stretch beyond the village. There were priests, and nuns, in particular one group—Raoul said they could be either the Maronite Sisters of the Holy Family or the Sisters of the Holy Hearts of Jesus and Mary—crisp and tall in their public regalia, shepherding a neat crocodile of girls. Leila from the back said: "Well, they could be the Maronite Sisters of St. Thérèse of the Child Jesus. I don't know. We are so irreligious." She gave that fat, thick chuckle of hers and continued chatting to the maids.

Raoul said: "Look! Many others doing it." He was pointing to a truck stacked with furniture being unloaded before a handsome villa. The owner's limousine, with loose clothing and cases, the trunk cover up, the doors wide open, was also being unloaded. We had already passed several such trucks and several such supervising proprietors, hot and agitated, gesturing orders.

"And it usually begins in a month's time from now?"

He nodded. He disliked redundant comment.

I was itching to ask the purpose of our journey. How to tease information out of Raoul? I began by reviewing in my own mind what I knew of our reasons for being in the car, starting, simplest of all, with the maids. One of them, Hoda, was Leila's maid, the sweet mountain girl who looked after their apartment and who came from the village to which we were going and was affianced to a villager there, a service-taxi driver—a brute, Leila called him. She, of course, apart from helping in the morning, had the best reason in the world for the trip.

The other maid, a much older woman, regularly worked for Sheik Nassib during his summer mountain sojourns in place of one of his town staff who went visiting relatives in Damascus. She too came from the higher village. The Sheik owned land up there, as well as, through his political office— he being the Deputy for all this district—having a lien on a great many families. She had come along to take Leila to her house, to load her up with jams and other presents, and would be returning with us later. There was also a suggestion that a cousin of hers was giving birth today.

So much from Leila's gossip over lunch.

Now Leila herself. Of course she was not in any way part

of the Sheik's household. She was his first cousin, her father Abdallah being a brother of his father Fuad, these in turn, with one other brother, Boulos, being the sons of Maroun Hadiri, a rich mountain farmer with a priestly cast of mind. (Formerly, there had been several priests in the family.) All three brothers had prospered in life, Abdallah in Egypt, Fuad in Beirut, founding the present merchant empire, and Boulos in Chicago until he had returned, shortly after World War Two, to found along with Badri (Nassib's younger brother) a banking side to the clan's ventures. Boulos was now the only man of that older generation still to be alive, and was a constant source of scandal, in Paris or Switzerland, making the columns with some gorgeous woman.

Children, brothers, cousins had proliferated. All these people were assiduously fecund. And though they fought among themselves, they helped one another with their special skills; and it was just here that Leila entered in. For Sheik Nassib's wife was much occupied, for the glory of the church, with good works (it also assisted her husband's image) so that details like seeing to their summer house were something of a tiresome problem for her. She evidently said: "Can't Leila see to it?" This request her husband smoothly relayed, knowing that good-hearted Leila would oblige and would feel privileged to do so.

For, yes, there was another twist to it. Leila had been married to a Cairo doctor; not a very prosperous union. He had neglected his practice and mysteriously died. Their only son was working in America. Leila had lacked the art of saving money; had all her life been generous to a fault, so that as a widow, suddenly, she needed money. Then, in 1956, Raoul and Leila had been thrown out of Egypt. Raoul had never learned to earn money. But at that point Nassib had stepped in and had invested what remained to them in property, adding a tidy sum of his own. So they owned this apartment block in the city with their own apartment on the seventh floor with its astounding view of sea and mountains. Leila, from the rents, was repaying the Sheik; but still his saving action remained. And all her life, it was certain, Leila would run to serve him in any little thing he mentioned.

So that accounted for Leila in the car.

I, temporarily in one of the apartments while some distant cousin was in Europe, and introduced there through a number of factors—though possibly the principal among them had been the Sheik's wish, once he knew of my connection with his son Robert, and with the journalist Hamid, to keep a controlling finger on me, to filter, he would see it, what I wrote about his country (never guessing that I would write about him)—had become really rather friendly with Raoul. There had been that first disastrous encounter; then amiability. He liked to take me along. And with Leila, I could always talk about Egypt.

So I was the observer, on the edge of the scene.

Then Raoul himself. He scoffed at the Hadiris. He could say dim things concerning their leader. (He was a wonderful source of secret information, given invariably in the form of satire.) But presumably when his name was called, he too rallied to the flag. How else explain? He was so very quietly, so very dutifully, intent on this errand.

I had not really grasped his position.

To prod, I began: "One might almost think we were running away from the first bombs! Speeding like this from the doomed city."

His face wrinkled. "Beirut won't be touched. I imagine the Israelis have taken our measure, Al Anwar, Al Muharrer, Al Shaab, and other such papers notwithstanding." He glanced at the back. They were talking in Arabic. "You know," he said, his face so quizzical it almost turned into a nut, "I don't mind your knowing what we are up to today!" The nut almost wrinkled to a pip. "In fact it would pass the time to explain."

"Forgive my curiosity."

He seemed to lose interest. As on many occasions, he could be shaking me off. The road was suddenly demanding again, not now from weight of contending traffic but from an intolerable succession of bends, on first one, then the other, side of the ravine. We were climbing to a visible paradise of orchards with snow slopes high behind them, but the gateway thereto was dauntingly narrow.

"Oh," he said, swinging the car to within inches of the unprotected edge, "it can be told in a word. I am only going because I want a certain house here. A retreat, let's call it, an old house that's been empty. But the man who is acting as go-between, who has all the power in his hands up here, even—and this is really the point—with regard to Nassib's voting list, has suddenly a grudge against our family, in particular against your good friend Robert. At all costs that has to be canceled. Nassib thinks so, whatever I am forced to promise in his name. And I think so, to get my house."

"Yes, obviously, you are chosen as the emissary."

"Yes. Also because, once in Egypt, my father helped this man's brother. In fact, the items on the ledger were balanced until Robert knocked them sideways. You should hear the rest of the clan on Robert! This paragon we all have to suffer. I don't really know what he has done this time, but something slighting, in his official capacity. That for the politician, his father, must be quite the last straw. We shall learn. And, let us hope, I shall also be able to show you over my future house!"

An uncharacteristic surge of excitement out of him almost took us into the ravine.

Not wise to probe further, but the passing reference to the voting list egged me on. One always heard the most lurid stories about behavior at elections in the outlying districts. Well, not only outside, in Beirut itself and the other main centers there were strong-arm men, and the all-pervasive supervision of the military, and money passed hands, and the promise of favors. But in more remote parts it was seemingly easier for people to be stopped on their way to the booths and for their papers suddenly to be found not in order. It was easier, favoring one of the candidates, for a tank to be stationed by the booth itself. And it was customary for the bargaining about favors and the price to be paid, so as to be linked with the candidacy of a powerful chieftain, a *zaim*—as was Nassib Hadiri, for all his modernistic trappings—to take the least sophisticated forms. For a fellow candidate to get onto his list, a winning list because Nassib could pay enough to make sure he got elected, that associate at the outset would pay Nassib about a hundred thousand pounds (Lebanese pounds: twenty-eight thousand American dollars). But once in the Chamber, he would hope to recoup his outlay in the space of a year. A good business machine, and therefore to be guarded against any hint of a wrench in the works. Hence Raoul's mission today.

So far, so good. But who was this man, this go-between, who held power in the district? I had imagined that all the power was Nassib's.

I asked this question, but Raoul slid away from it. As we neared our destination, he was evasive again, almost as if no moments of trust had ever passed between us. He replied, but with words that told nothing. He began talking in Arabic to Leila and the maids, joining in that other conversation. Then the village, shifting position dramatically as we came upon it over a rise, claimed our attention. There was a statue by the church. "That's the grandfather of the man we are visiting. Hanged by the Turks for taking a lead in resisting their tax collectors. In those days he controlled the Hadiris.

Though he in turn was answerable to one of the old heredi-
tary nobility, one of the emirs who ruled this region as part
of the Imarah, or princedom, of Lebanon. You see, we have
come up rather recently. In these people's eyes, we are still
on trial."

So, once you had ceased asking a question, Raoul, per-
versely, answered it.

The man we were visiting had been *mukhtar*, or mayor,
but had resigned this office to one of his relatives. He was
now simply a village elder. His house overlooked the *saha*,
the space, before the principal church, and it was a two-floor
house. The vaulted ground floor, originally a shelter for
animals and fodder, was now being used as a shop. He lived
with his family on the upper floor, reached by an outside
stone stairway and a richly carved stone portal, the topmost
feature of which was a cross. The roof was tiled and steeply
inclined, and this, I was to learn, about eighty years before
had replaced a flat roof of poplar beams covered with stone
chips and clay. This composition was rolled each year to
waterproof it before winter. At the back of the house were
a well-kept garden blooming with roses and other small
flowers and, recalling the bygone silk industry, a single mul-
berry tree. The elder's orchards lay below the village, and
he was also the owner of land higher up, where a flock of
goats and sheep were minded. He had one or two commercial
interests. But possibly he had seen better days.

The interior of the house was traditionally planned, with
a long central chamber and smaller side rooms. At the end
was a balcony with pointed arches, giving a view of the
church and the road and, beyond the village, of the lush
green grove, the *merj*, where the watercourse came down
out of a cavern just higher up. This was a deep valley village,
inturned, without a view of the sea.

We sat in the central chamber near the window. The demeanor of the elder, a rather foxy old man with grey moustache and a sallow complexion, was from the outset excessively courteous. He said that our visit honored his dwelling and that it was ours for as long as we chose. He mentioned Raoul's father with affection, and with great deference he lauded Raoul, as a poet, as a life-giver and standard-bearer. Raoul was equally soft-tongued, and they both wove their speech together without otherwise mentioning the Hadiris. Leila and the maids had gone elsewhere. We were sitting in deep, cane-backed chairs, and the elder on the long couch by the wall, though, again out of deference, he was sitting on it tentatively, leaning forward to catch each word, and only tentatively was he sipping his coffee, inquiring if ours was to our taste with just that touch of rose water added. French-speaking fortunately, and with an interplay of silence and an endless stock of preliminary clichés, he was no doubt taking his visitor's measure, as the visitor would be taking his. My presence did not seem to deflect him.

Then he asked my view of the Middle East crisis. Thinking to please him, I simply repeated a part of what I had heard that morning: that the Arabs had come by an easy victory. But he shook his head, and in a quickened voice he launched into more oracular speech. The Third World War would shortly be upon us. That had been certain, he said, when the Syrians, who were mischief-makers and utterly demoralized, had encouraged the fedayeen raids against Israel. The Jews had responded. Each party had backers, and neither Russia nor America could now climb down. Hadn't the Russians sent cruisers through the Bosporus? Wasn't the Sixth Fleet awaiting them? Out there—he gestured away from the mountains—the nuclear death might already have started.

"You should be spared up here, God willing." Raoul earnestly seemed to be hoping this. "But tell me, why should any fighting begin? Many people say that the worst is over."

"They fool themselves. They do not know the Syrians. All those Arabs are drunk with the thought of drinking their coffee in Tel Aviv. They will slaughter the Jews; they have sworn to do so. Then America, then Russia, will not stand aside." He tugged at his moustache. I was particularly taken, apart from his appetite for the worst, by his way of castigating the Arabs as though he himself was something different.

Though admittedly Raoul could do this too. And others of his family. Perhaps many of the Maronites rather easily referred to "those Arabs."

"Do you think the Jews have a case?" I asked the elder. It was not often one dared to ask this, but his attitude seemed equivocal.

"What must be said in Beirut," he answered, "need not always be said in this village. All through our history we have fought the Muslims. They would crush us if they could. And now we observe that the Jews are faced with a similar threat. I do not like the Jews. I do not like the Muslims. I remember that in 1860 the Druzes, at the instigation of Ottoman soldiers, butchered almost a third of my family. I have not experienced Jewish soldiers."

"May that never happen," murmured Raoul.

"I remember," the elder was warming to his subject, "the famine up here in the First World War. They wanted to starve the Christian Mountain. Many parents had to bury their children. I remember still the cry that was heard: 'Oh my God, I am so hungry!' I was twenty when it ended. I have never walked well. I think that we should work to take this country completely out of the Muslim world!" He had forgotten the coming nuclear solution.

"But half of Lebanon's population is Muslim."

"Frankly, I have never got used to that arithmetic. We are Christian on the Mountain. Why bow to the Arabs? I have never got used to the ways of Beirut."

As if at a signal they were talking in Arabic. They could not return to casual pleasantries. The word Beirut seemed to catapult them into the more intimate discussion awaiting. The elder's tone, though unfailingly suave, became that of repeated re-emphasis, the movements of his palms, open, extended, pulled back vertically, winding around to leave only his thumb and index finger unfolded, these lightly tapping each other, all spoke of a sense of outrage, of custom affronted, of pleading with his listener to consult honor and to feel ashamed. Poor Raoul was undergoing the treatment.

I looked about and sipped at the glass of homemade *araq* set beside the coffee. A girl had served us and disappeared. She could have been wife, daughter, or maid. There were murmurings from behind shut doors. A silver-framed photograph perched on top of a free-standing marble pillar showed an austere wedding assembly, the oldest member wearing baggy black breeches with voluminous folds hanging at the crotch and a jodhpur tight fitting to the legs. He wore a collarless shirt and a fancy waistcoat, a cummerbund, and one could tell from his moustache that he was some ancient relative of the elder's. Another photograph showed a crew-cut student against the background of an American campus. There was a calendar from Coca-Cola. There was a cabinet of assorted china and magazines on a ledge beneath. There were broad *kilims* on the tiled floor, embroidered floor cushions, and a gaudy pouf. At first the room seemed to have no unity, but this gradually asserted itself, perhaps beneath the continuous flow of the elder's softly demanding voice.

His foxy look had been largely replaced by a blander type of committeeman's expression, possibly as his argument reached its apex and Raoul showed a willingness to yield. Raoul was not answering much. He had coiled his small body up tightly, except for his long expressive fingers drooping before him then flicking up, waving up and down like sensitive antennae acknowledging this or that contention,

while his gaze was intently fixed on the speaker as though to
hold a mirror there. I don't know how long they debated.
It only seemed like a minute or two, for a flow of Arabic is
rhythmic and soothing. The mountain air was crystal sweet.
There was a hum of transistor radios from the village, and
the occasional shot of a gun being fired. I had long since
lost my westernized timing, had regained—for I had formerly
lived in these countries—a feeling for time as inseparable from
the immediate event in which I was involved, from that
event's determination.

Everything in its own time.

The attitude of painstaking craftsmen.

Like two craftsmen finally satisfied, and I equally with the
part of waiting, Raoul and the elder had clasped hands. More
coffee came. Raoul explained that we were shortly going to
see his house. One of the family had been sent for Leila. We
could all go in the car together.

In English his voice had a dry undertone, passing some
sort of comment on our host and on what must now be
relayed to the Sheik. But, switching to French, he began to
discourse, as though it equally were a leading topic, on the
care being taken with Hoda, the maid, to insure that she
escaped harm in the city. She was chaperoned. The films she
saw were censored. Her betrothed, though allowed to call
at the apartment, was not allowed to take her to cafés. Indeed,
she had never ridden in his cab, and she was not allowed to
wear short skirts or be seen on the beach in a bathing suit.
Truth was, in my view, Raoul and Leila behaved in a miser-
able way to their maid, like warders, always keeping her in,
like slavers, to deliver the goods undamaged. One recalled
those items in the local press about maids who, in desperation
at being caged in, threw themselves off top-floor balconies.
Against that, however, there were other maids who did so
much as go out with a man, perhaps sat beside him talking

in a café or were seen in his car, or beside him at the cinema, and they, and this was the most lurid tradition still very active in Lebanese life, were promptly disposed of by father or brothers. There was the case recently of the brother who had heard that his sister had been seen in some friend's car (never mind that it was only negotiating the main street); he had promptly chased her, and, because she had been warned, he had only caught up with her at the airport. There he had neatly decapitated her and returned with her head in a plastic bag. Another man, a father, with the pretense of leading his erring daughter back to their home, on the way, in a wood, had taken a stone and bashed her brains out.

So, though poor Hoda's slavery was pitiable, her sweet little face going with a character of the very highest sort, it was possibly understandable—rumor and passion and the family ego still being so rancid. Indeed, the elder, who was seemingly concerned as he had advised her father that she would be safe in Leila's service, was nodding satisfaction, only adding perfunctorily that Beirut was a pit of evil.

"Ah, it is a shameless life! The rich are to blame. Even the Sheik, God praise his wisdom, needs to keep an eye on his kindred. Even here our clean ways are disappearing. For those who go down to the city return with a different spirit in their hearts. This man, this fiancé of Hoda, with his taxi, he and his like are a thorn in the flesh. They lack respect. I would not choose him as a son."

"But he has his uses, surely?" queried Raoul. "Each day he brings news. He is a link politically?"

"Oh, he has his uses," said the elder grudgingly, and again he changed the subject.

This exchange, too, Raoul explained when we were finally clear of the village. Nothing had been wasted in their conversation for all its shifts and interpolations and the seeming love of the ancient proverb. It was a deft dance through a sky of moods, each dancer, in turn, tricked to seek the other, to resolve the next step forward. The elder, Raoul said, was a fine performer. All Arabs loved to play this game.

"You see, in this and the other Mountain villages, there is the stay-at-home group who are the élite, the conservatives, who are versed in lore and genealogies, and in the price of a bride or a *dunum* of land. They are skilled in farming. They are good at mediation. They are still respected for their family position in the now defunct feudal hierarchy. That's our elder. He is a dying type. But he still has his finger in everything. . . .

"Then comes the more liberal group of returned emigrants, who are men with ready money and a world outlook. Their philosophy is more empirical. They are taking over the running of the district. And in the main, also, they are supporting Nassib against contenders from among the conservatives, from, let us say, a descendent of the emirs thinking to make a democratic comeback. Here, you see, it was the elder's cousins, one of whom is now the *mukhtar*, all men grown rich in America, who pulled the elder across the line and with him a decisive number of voters. That is why he is vital for Nassib. Of course, that is all fixed among the families long before elections. The booth is incidental. . . .

"Lastly, a new group has appeared: indeterminate still but potentially powerful, of whom our service-taxi driver is typical. These are villagers working in the city, forever commuting or living down there except for a month or two in summer. They are busy making money and less than their fathers are they willing to enter government service. They are better educated, socially ambitious, and politically they like the Kataeb, the most militant of the Christian parties. That's very likely because, living in the city, they sense the pulse of the Muslim mob!

"The interesting point is that the elder is threatening to go in now with the Kataeb. As you know, cousin Farid is a member, and Nassib, at his level, has working arrangements. But here, at the grass roots, it would be awkward. It would whittle away the Sheik's bloc vote. And Hoda's fiancé, though the elder scorned him, is in fact their daily link man. He and the elder have in fact an understanding, though that connects with the police also. They are both 'eyes' for the Deuxième Bureau."

"How complicated!"

"What community isn't? One could add a lot more, in fact, to the jigsaw puzzle. All I am showing is that the references to Hoda, to her taxi man, and to other odd characters all fitted in. By the time we had finished we had worked a most satisfying arabesque."

"So what, initially, was the elder's complaint?"

"Against the family? Against Robert? Frankly, it was not all revealed. The elder was threatening this new alliance between the older families and the Kataeb, or 'this young people's group,' as he was calling it. Various specious reasons. He is mainly establishing a bargaining position for next year's elections. How much more he will get from Nassib depends on Nassib's counteracting contacts. Luckily I was able to offer something by giving a definite date for the clinic, vaguely promised to the village before. The elder liked that. His tone moderated. As for his specific complaint, it would seem that on a recent visit to Robert's Ministry, Robert personally evaded seeing him. That is an affront. He waited all morning. As you know, among Arabs, in theory at least, all doors are eventually open. The elder was seeking promotion for a nephew, which, all too likely, Robert knew! Well, I rather suspect there is more to it. But even so, it was a jolt to his pride. It's this gap between the generations. The old think all is gained through influence; the young are trying to establish merit. Robert is right. But the Sheik will not think so."

"So you have promised this nephew's promotion also?"

"Certainly!" Raoul gloried in his handiwork. "Let Nassib and Robert sort it out between them."

Would they ever? In the last two months I had seen enough of the conflict separating father and son, political boss and civil servant, to wonder if they grasped each other's language. Robert had sworn never again to be a tool of this petty nepotism. His father had blandly intimated that his son, when tested, would fall into line. A test for some time had been avoided. Now, suddenly, it had been sprung upon them.

Raoul, clearly, guessed at something further—intrigue being the breath of life here.

"So you are satisfied with today's outcome?"

"Naturally. Didn't I receive my reward?"

He had indeed. When Leila had joined us—but not Hoda yet, for she was visiting the house where a child was soon expected—we had driven to the highest ground in the village and there inspected the tumbledown dwelling that Raoul had set his heart on.

Again the warm patina, a kind of dusky yellow, of the beautifully cut mountain stone. It was a two-part building. We had approached from above, between well-gardened terraces. In contrast to them stood the old house, the part at the left long and rectangular, its flat roof collapsed. What looked to be a vaulted chamber there beneath, with pillared recesses on either side, running from leveled earth at the back to a front terrace overlooking the village, was largely hidden by rubble and brambles, tin cans, and rotting paper. The children who had suddenly sprung from nowhere, crying on the placid afternoon air, seemed to use the place for their games.

But attached to this abandoned structure was a square

tower, which, approached from the back, presented us first with a gradual stairway rising through a top, commodious step to a deep porch, double-arched and roomy. Indeed, it was an ideal summer room. And at the back of this were two adjacent doors leading to rooms with the front view again. The walls of the tower were high and cool inside. It had a flat roof too, but in good repair.

"Fine," chuckled Raoul, climbing a ladder onto the roof and stamping the property "a wonderful place! I have a Persian *liwan* as a living room; or is there something Mamluk about it? A Crusader tower; or could it be Roman? We have been so eclectic. So many armies have left us something in the wake of retreat. Look at that view! Who first beheld it? Some Canaanite shepherd? Some hewer of cedar? And then perhaps there was a merchant or courtier fleeing the summer heat of Byblus. Later, much later, after Greeks and Romans, there was a Shia farmer planting his fruit trees. Or a Druze intoning his secret prayers. Last of all, certainly, came the Maronites, colonizing south out of Qadisha. And so that brings us to the present owner."

"Which is now you?"

"Not exactly yet. The present owner emigrated. It has been difficult to reach him because there was a feud. He mortgaged this house to buy his ticket, and his cousins claim that he never paid them back. At last he has proved that he has paid them back, but now they say that they have maintained the terraces, and need the building as a storeroom. A storeroom! Grasping peasants. The elder should fix them, because, as it happens, he is also mediating as part of a committee to effect a compromise between them and neighbors in a two-year-old demarcation dispute. Such is village life. Here he comes . . . and the peasant."

Raoul need not have worried. He had earned a settlement. If any small point had still been in question, now, with a sign of his hand, the elder resolved it. The peasant nodded and gave his word. Raoul got a cluster of apple trees and the produce of two rows of terracing. The peasant would repair and maintain the building. There was ample water. They could live like brothers. To seal this, the price rose five percent.

"Well, quite a high price. They are wise to it nowadays. I am not the first to come from the city!" Raoul grinned ruefully. He had paid "like an American," Leila chided him. But she too was pleased. It was a second home she could furnish for him, where she could visit him when he was in retreat.

"How peaceful it is in the country," she eulogized. "I think, you know, that we had better go back. It will soon be dark. There is still much traffic." She looked across the ravine apprehensively. She repeated her remarks in French to the elder, who protested, saying a meal was prepared for us. His womenfolk had been preparing it. Raoul, laughing, took him by the arm and replied in very rapid Arabic. Protestations continued. The peasant stood watching us, partly, perhaps, trying to visualize the sort of trouble he might expect in future. He and Raoul clasped each other's shoulders. Then we got into the car and departed.

Back in the village we looked for Hoda, but the whole village was gathering near the house where the new baby had been expected. Already people were carrying gifts, chickens prominent among these. A drum was being beaten, a flute, a guitar were adding to the celebration. A son had been born. It had already been swaddled, by the midwife sure of a handsome payment, and was being inspected by the family within. "*Mabrouk,*" cried the elder, pressing forward, "*Inshâ'llâh bislam.*" May God keep him safe. "*Mabrouk! Mabrouk!*" Blessed be the son! With joyous gravity the village exulted.

"So now you must stay," the elder insisted. "It is a sign from God. There will be no holocaust. He has given us a sign. He will calm the Great Powers. We must eat and give thanks together."

"We will eat with you in a week's time," answered Raoul. "Tonight the Sheik awaits us at table."

"So be it." He appeared suddenly indifferent.

But, before we left, in addition to the jams and herbs and fats from Leila's sources, from the elder's house we took fresh mountain bread, in thin sheets like bundles of scrolls, and fresh *labneh*, the cream cheese. To make sure that we did not go hungry on the way, and to accommodate our indecent haste, we were each handed a parting sandwich made from this bread spread with olive oil and thyme and sesame and filled with cheese—an *arous*, or bride, it was seemingly called. It was a parting jest between the elder and Raoul, for, now that Raoul would be entering the village, it was not right for him to stay a bachelor.

"Marry the daughter of a good family, though she be an old maid," he quoted me. "He must have some relative ready!"

"What a glorious day," intoned Leila.

Hoda's eyes were full of mountain joy.

Raoul, like a service-taxi driver, speeded into the gloom of the ravine, munching his sandwich, one hand on the wheel. "Careful!" One had to say it to him. He shrugged. His mood required some bravado. Then he slowed. "You are right. I must still report and be ready for the Sheik to have changed his tactics! We had better, I suppose, survive for the war." He was regaining his usual crisp intonation. "At least, to note whose prediction was nearest. Shall we listen to what they are saying from Cairo? Or Damascus? There can't be much difference."

He switched on the radio. A prolonged snarl came over.

Then the next station gave martial music, then a voice like a hammer battered us.

A week ago, Raoul interpreted, they were saying simply that they pitied the Jews. Tonight they were saying that the Jews were dead. As good as dead. The Arabs had decided.

We drove on through the Lebanese mountains. Crags, precipices, swooned away from us.

It was dark as we climbed through the last gorge, twisting with the pack of cars and pedestrians animating the village high streets, with everywhere the radios blaring propaganda. But topping the rise, then descending sharply to where the Sheik's mountain villa stood, there was light still coming off the sea, in pink-purple bands near to shore and a pink-orange glimmer toward the horizon. Winds had blown the mist from the city and from the straggle of suburbs along the coast and up the lower slopes at our feet. This complex in the twilight had a ghostly look, a ghostly shimmer dissolving suddenly into a single purple smudge. Then it was black, like the hill about us, and an array of lights was suddenly apparent. The main highways teemed with vehicles. The center of Beirut glowed and looked solid. Through a sky suddenly alive with stars an airliner winked its approach. The transposition from day to night had seemed only a matter of seconds.

We entered the courtyard, prettily lit so that the fountain and the carved stone window boxes and the filagree lanterns and other such features in turn drew one's eye. One might have expected a taped voice to be giving out the history of the place, knowing the Hadiri love of devices. But then so much had been purchased elsewhere, from other dwellings, and added for effect. The Hadiris, although their family tree with its priestly stems predated the Crusades, were, as notables, among the newly arrived. Even the title of Sheik displayed a certain nerve on Nassib's part, though no one who had met him could doubt his right to it. All, finally, depended on the man.

By night, as day, the view was tremendous, though now largely of a star-filled realm. The coastal strip popped with lights, but this scene was meager beside the brilliance of the heavens, where each constellation seemed to have been mounted for special display on jeweler's velvet, and lesser known clusters abounded. And below there was a silvery sheen on the waters, carrying the eye away to the west, mapping a course to Europe and beyond. With the high mountains dismissing the interior, one naturally looked outward here—as had been the inclination of the littoral since the time, as one's friends were apt to tell one, of their famous Phoenician ancestors.

Cousin Farid, in particular, of the Hadiris made great play of the Phoenician ancestry. It was part of his armory against "the Arabs."

Who in fact had those early navigators been? It was natural to ask the question again, staring out on the star-lit waters. The earliest recorded inhabitants had been Canaanites, early Bronze Age people who, as traders and craftsmen, had shared a common Semitic culture with their neighbors to the south and east in what became known as Palestine and Syria. All of them at some time would have come out of the vast Arabian peninsula, and in turn were invaded from north or south by Sumerians, Hittites, Hyksos, and Egyptians.

Then other invaders from southern Europe had mingled with the local stock, coming by boat and adding their skills to those of the sailors and boat builders trekking over from the Persian Gulf. Byblus, Aradus, Ugarit, and, following these, Sidon and Tyre (from the fifteenth to the ninth centuries B.C.) rose as the great centers of trade and industry in glass and ivory and metals. They were great centers of wealth and omnivorous culture, beginning to launch their trading ships beyond the earlier coastal runs to points to the west, to Greece, and North Africa, and out into the Atlantic.

It was the Greeks who termed these traders Phoenicians, from the Greek word *phoinix*, purple-red—the purple-dyed cloth that the traders brought was among their most coveted products; and so it was that as Phoenicians these thoroughly mixed, latter-day Canaanites made the Mediterranean their lake. They commanded the then east-west traffic, they developed and passed on the alphabet, they luxuriated in orgiastic rites, and gave something of their music to the Hebrews and of their myth and drama to the early Greeks. They were a wide-eyed, stocky people, with strong, black-bearded chins, superlative as merchants and leaders of fashion, loving wealth, intrigue, and pleasure.

In fact, and the Hadiris would smile as one acknowledged it, they had been at least the spiritual ancestors of the Lebanese men of affairs of today. And that despite all later invasions, from Mesopotamia, Persia, Rome, despite the adoption of Christianity, despite the long Muslim interregnum, the Phoenician spirit had subtly prevailed, infecting all who came to this coast.

"It's that I feel Phoenician," young Maurice had laughed, following swiftly in the path of his uncles. "That is what I mean when I say Lebanese." All the Hadiris worked on this image.

We had hardly settled ourselves in the courtyard when Sheik Nassib's chauffeur appeared. Besides driving the car, he was a special emissary, chief bodyguard, and quite often the butler. More sinister still, his brother who was a butcher with a shop in the Achrafiyeh quarter of Beirut, where the leading Christian families resided, was one of the last Christian *qabadāy* in the old sense of the term, a thug or killer. This gentleman had been known to spring out on the pavement at the sight of some man he disfavored, someone who had been "throwing a shadow across his shop," and threaten to cut him into pieces. He was an expert hand at crushing people's knuckles. He had been active in times of civil disorder: in the civil fighting of 1958 he had carved crosses on Muslim foreheads, and he was always a factor at election time. Similarly, there were Muslim *qabadāy*, the toughs of the Muslim quarters. The species as a whole, however, was declining in Lebanon.

All the chauffeur wanted, to our relief, was to tell us that the Sheik would be coming for certain, that Raoul should await him, and that in the meantime an adequate repast should be prepared. He had brought two hampers of food in the car lest there were not enough in the house. The maids should get busy. Half the clan was coming. The latest news in Beirut was bad.

"Are they staying up here?" asked Raoul innocently. Usually he managed to ignore this chauffeur.

No, it would only be for a conference. They had passed the afternoon at Bhamdoun with Madame's side of the family. All Christians were alarmed but firm.

Raoul declined to examine this statement. He waited for the chauffeur to remove himself. Soon after, we heard the purr of departure as the great car thrust to the road. Hoda brought us *araq* with ice. We reckoned that an hour of peace remained to us.

It seemed a good moment to discuss Raoul's poetry, to discover a little further why the epicurean visions of his youth, the *"calme, luxe, et volupté"* intensely pursued in symbolist fragments had turned so markedly to ashes and gall. His verse now, though more supple and direct, a process in part of divesting his language of forms borrowed from other poets, presented only a world of absurdities and of pity

for those who found themselves in it. Why pity? One wanted
to ask him. From what standpoint did he introduce pity?

But Raoul, perhaps suddenly nervous or tired from the
responsibilities of the day, unexpectedly now chose to talk
politics, to throw out disconnected observations that it was
difficult to think he believed himself. Then he paced about
the courtyard. He called up to Leila, who was sitting up
there in the women's sitting room, and when she did not
appear, he became impatient. "Where are you?" he cried. He
stood stock still with nerves. "Leila, Leila, what are you
doing?"

"I am here, Raoul, *cher*." Her large person, her stoical face
loomed above us. A smile gradually spread toward him.

Then we noticed the small Armenian beside her—Sarkoubian, her private spy, who had been one of her visitors in
Cairo and had followed to knock on her door here too. He
was a peddler with family in all these countries. He still wore
the tarbush his father had worn from the days when it had
commanded respect in Egypt.

"What does he want?" Raoul barked.

"He says the gypsies are traveling north. They are filling
the roads out of south Lebanon."

Grunt. "Mmm, that means that eventually they will meet
the Armenians coming south from Turkey!"

The little Armenian grinned with pleasure at being teased
by Monsieur Raoul. His immense nose shone.

"But it is serious," she urged. "It may mean that after all
America cannot stop this war."

Raoul looked mollified by her naïveté. "We are quite safe
here," he reassured her. "Not even the Armenians are going
to suffer. Eh, Sarkoubian? What a chance for you, eh, if
Tigranes the Great were alive today?"

Sarkoubian seemed to understand him and twinkled darkly.

He retreated out of sight, and Leila followed, chatting away. She usually came to life in the evenings.

She soon had more company surrounding her. A bevy of "Les Jeunes Filles" arrived. One heard their noisy car pull up. This time it was Marie-Rose and Yola with their cousin Lulu's friend, Coco. "Les Jeunes Filles en Fleur," as Raoul called them, not with much originality, were mostly cousins and the children of Hadiris, and all were preoccupied with having a good time in the process of being lined up for husbands. As their various mothers were rather dictatorial, obsessed, they would say, with virtue and money (though equally they were obsessed with the latter themselves), they turned for sympathy to Aunty Leila, and for an alibi in their escapades. "We were at Aunty Leila's," was the explanation for some outing in the late afternoon. Aunty-from-Egypt was their nickname for her.

Giggles. Laughter. Heavy featured faces. They went straight up to Leila and appeared leaning on the balcony, their hair hanging in long loose coils or partly pinned up, so great was its abundance. They were indeed teenage Juliets with fat cheeks and soft mouths and eyes, though possibly with too much make-up there enlarging those already generous attractions. They were not stopping long. They were restless with excitement. Some fabulous party was scheduled in town, and after that they would go to the Casino. They were not too sure why they had come up here.

"To see you, Aunty. And oh, it's Mother! She would like us here, but what would we do here? We have been in attendance most of the day. All that boring political talk!" It was Yola speaking, Nassib's youngest daughter and just a year out of school. "We have eaten so many cakes and sweets. It is impossible to go on. Explain. Plead for us."

It was still as difficult to see why they had come, except

perhaps to learn at firsthand the extent of the villa's summer preparations. They were staring down at Raoul and me as though we were captive fish in a pond, although they had politely bade us good evening. "I suppose," Yola cried down to him, "that you are enjoying it. You love these awful situations such as wars!"

"Do I? Is that my reputation?" He was icy. Between Yola and he there was continual challenge, which related to her sister Christiane. It stemmed from some mischievous misunderstanding. But then Les Jeunes Filles, though hardly deprived of emotional stimulation, seemed always to be manufacturing new emotions. A way of filling in their time.

"We have to go." They were now keen on departure. They fussed about Leila, saying that they could never have passed a whole day without coming to hug her—and that truthfully might explain their appearance. Then they clattered downstairs, waved, and were gone.

"No, I fear I don't see either what brought them tearing up here!" Raoul laughed. "Of course, for them, the effort's the same as for driving round the block. They don't notice the traffic. They most likely needed to get the crisis out of their hair before going to their savage little party. They'll be twisting and jerking at the same hour as Arab soldiers fall asleep in the desert. But they can sleep tomorrow morning."

"So you think zero hour is striking?"

He shrugged. "I don't think, as you do, that the CIA has encouraged Israel. Israel will simply be taking advantage of the ham-handed Arab deployment, which I, as you know, attribute to the Russians, though possibly Nasser forced the pace. At Aqaba. That could be his stroke."

"But that is the stroke that has made war certain!"

He shrugged. "You say, and I say, through different reasoning, that other interests wished to precipitate a Middle East conflict during this year—before there was a chance of the Arabs winning. Could they ever win? I anticipate your question. By first losing their souls, they could, and, without that extremity, possibly also by accumulating planes and missiles and launching them all in one surprise attack. But at that point they would have lost their souls! So now the minutes will tick away until General Dayan takes the initiative. It could start tonight. He likes night-fighting. It's an historic hour. This will change our history."

"I do wish you could all negotiate."

"Exactly; you share the western thinking, as, I believe, do the Russians today. It doesn't much matter who has done the plotting. Russia, America, Israel, each believes in the present showdown, rather than something stickier later, in order to shake the Arab mentality, to shock it into coming to terms with the century. Superficials apart, we are still medieval."

"You are among the remaining humanist cultures—Islamic orthodoxy notwithstanding."

"And modern Powers find that uncomfortable! Well, these currents are often subconscious. The *zeitgeist*. The economic imperatives. Then there are those who turn away from it— like the young western hippies who are feebly trying to recreate the kind of sensual Time that we have never lost. We are saturated with our sensuality. Like animals. . . ." He was becoming upset. For all his cultivated western upbringing, Raoul could suddenly hate the West.

We were saved from awkwardness by the next contingent. A smooth-sounding car. It would be Sami's Mercedes. Of the Sheik's three sons, Sami was the playboy, the gambler and dabbler in small-time deals, who nonetheless somehow managed to retain a key position at the heart of the family. He lacked Robert's seriousness and bureaucratic brilliance. He had none of the big business flair of his cousins Maurice, Elie, and Georges. He lacked Christiane's warmth and her wayward intelligence. He had intelligence too, and charm and presence, but all of the most predictable kind. His hold was baffling, unless it derived from his being his mother's favorite son. For her and her religion he was the lost sheep, the favorite of God, and he flourished on this. Even his uncles, all capable men, would sidle up for his good opinion. He mesmerized the clan like a pocket Satan, and indeed his one clear service had been to help with the clan's success at elections through some of his deep underground contacts. Yet when his father the Deputy appeared, Sami usually made himself scarce.

Besides the Mercedes, he had a German wife, a cool beauty much photographed locally. Together they had once run a night club. They figured at all the smart parties, and not only among Maronite Christians. They were a part of that pleasure-loving élite that was simply bored by confessional division. It was said Sami had helped to put Muslims in power through the same machinery that he offered his family. He had access to such personal information through some of the property he owned in town. His life seemed to sail before the wind.

Raoul loathed him. So his entry attracted all of Raoul's mounting spleen. "Are you staying for dinner? Leila's upstairs."

"My dear Raoul, we are dining at the Nabkis'. That's five minutes on. Such a good idea for people to be moving to the mountains now." He touched my hand. "You know my wife, Brigitte? You must dine with us soon. Perhaps in Tel Aviv, as our friend Shukairy is now promising the Arabs!"

"I am surprised that you haven't enlisted, Sami. You could become the family's first colonel." Then Raoul turned more sweetly to the wife. "Nice to see you, Brigitte, on your feet again, all ready, I suppose, for those eager photographers." His tone was warm, and it drew her aside from her quite impossible husband.

Sami's amusement deepened.

Leila came down. She made a fuss over the couple. She was by now aloft with the evening's excitement. She bade Hoda bring drinks. From Sami she reckoned to hear the latest and juiciest scandal; she would protest, of course, then repeat it to everyone. "Why are you not staying for dinner? The Sheik told me that all the family would be present."

"I already have Papa's permission." He paused. "Which is more than Christiane has sought. She may be dining in the opposite camp! Speaking, of course, as between Arabs."

Raoul frowned, and Leila clucked. This question of Christiane was too serious, as it touched the Sheik, for light banter. Neither cared to discuss it publicly. Sami could tell them of what he liked, except this scandal concerning his sister. Well, they wanted to know, but not from him, and, seeing him there gloating, one understood them. But he was relentless as a mischief-maker, and he continued: "As for Hamid's wife, where, I wonder, will she be dining?"

A few more such trifles, more drinks, and they departed, departed as, at last, the Sheik's party appeared, the first of the cousins gliding in. "That was bad," said Raoul. "He is really a scoundrel. I'm afraid all the stories about him are true."

"I pity Christiane. . . ." Leila's voice trailed off.

"She is the elf of the family."

"And her father's favorite. . . ."

They both shrugged. There was no point in pitying. And the man who would not thank them for it was approaching. The clan, even in entering, looked united, filling up the courtyard space with the quiet precision of a corps de ballet, then continuing, led by the Sheik and his mother, the old lady with a stick whom his arm was supporting, up the stairway to the women's salon. Even cousin Farid, with his long stride and his wild stare, had this precision. And we also followed, for the prelude to greetings, or to breaking away into any kind of group, was that the old lady should be seated in her chair, her shawl and stick clutched as insignia. The feeling, as one joined them mounting the stairway, was not of joining any courtier chorus, so purposeful and individual was each of them, but (still supposing it to have been a ballet) of joining a guerrilla band returning from one of their raids to their mountain lair. The only adjustment one's eye must make concerned their dress: they wore elegant suitings, white shirts, gold cufflinks, and, of course, if not quite millionaires, they were rich.

But the impression remained of soft-footed commandos.

Minutes later there was a buzz of small talk, Hoda and the chauffeur serving the drinks with little saucers of pistachios and almonds. Only three of the wives were present, and none of the younger generation of children. There were various cars outside, but just the one chauffeur; the other chauffeurs, perhaps less trustworthy, had been left in town and the owners had driven. Cousin Farid looked very excited, very much in the mood of the day. Badri and Michel and their elder sons (except for the invariably quicksilver Maurice) were guarded, heavy, obscurely smiling, and Badri was softly clicking his beads.

They were all speaking French. I was standing behind Badri. He was speaking about some loan a firm wanted. "They all want loans. They won't get them now. There'll be some bankrupt stock on offer. *Inshâ'llâh!* But the omens are against it. An inauspicious month." Badri from behind did not show any neck. He was a broad man; one could see him revolving as a carved puppet on an old town clock. One knew that he was immensely cautious and quiet, the more so as his son Maurice developed, and yet his financial flair was prodigious. As banker to the clan he underwrote their security, and yet he could never have replaced Nassib.

Possibly too much of their priestly ancestry kept him still as the backroom boy.

It was a very pleasant room with high white walls and two large Persian carpets hanging. On the tiled floor there was a variety of rugs all squarely side by side. There was a tall wood stove standing free with the flue running back and above a shelf packed with books, plants, and antiques. Otherwise the furniture consisted of a corner settee for six persons with four other chairs facing round a table, and smaller tables each with chairs, and a few deep chairs, so that all together thirty people could be seated. There was plenty of space for walking about. On the corner table there was a dish offering fifteen brands of cigarettes, and it was just opposite this display of largess that the old lady, Fuad's widow, was seated, and next to her, her son Nassib and her very devout daughter-in-law.

Nassib. The Sheik. What marked him out as being the leader in this assembly? He was a big man, of medium height, the height again lost on account of his bulk. But in his case it was a prize fighter's bulk, very tough, very rugged. And he also had a bulky jowl, overstated eyebrows, big hairy hands that moved in firm yet fluent gestures. He was extremely affable when greeting people, at once absorbed in their affairs, till you saw that in part it was a cloak enabling him to make the calculations and adjustments, as with all Lebanese at lightning speed, that would hand him some new advantage. He made use of everyone, with determination, and yet with some appeal to higher principles that shone forth from his speech and face. One could not say what these were exactly, beyond the proverbs and clichés and charm. Yet one listened to and watched him and felt encouraged by the progress of all that he had a hand in. He was a leader, a proved and successful leader. Perhaps he wore the aura of command. At moments one thought one was also seeing, written into him, a trail of disappointments, of buffetings and defeats as well as victories; then he noticed your eye and, fast as a chameleon, he had taken on a rather waggish look. He was a local politician, after all.

He acted with great deference to his mother, quite possibly his most basic emotion.

We were quickly at dinner; no time was being wasted. There was only the chauffeur to serve us. Raw *kibbeh*—the ubiquitous crushed wheat pounded, it always seemed, for hours together with cubes of lamb and onion (one could say that along with demolition drilling and horn blowing this domestic sound gave the Lebanese morning its character)— was served with beans and a mixed salad and further separate sprigs of mint. They were all the most tremendous eaters. One added oil and yogurt to taste and filled in with olives and bread and also uncooked beans at this season. But however much one ate one could be certain that one's neighbor, be that man or woman, was eating more. They pressed food on one; they were regally hospitable; and they talked ten to the dozen as they ate. But then from the heaped dishes that remained—for there was never less than the most showy abundance—they took further gargantuan shares.

Nassib had fitted in Raoul beside him, and besides watching us all at the table with that quick, clear, all-absorbent look, so that to left and right, with complete sympathy, he could enter into any conversation, changing style before our eyes— the most consummate actor—he was listening through one drooped ear to Raoul. I was reminded of the time when I had seen him in his office, and he had been briefing me and simultaneously conversing on two telephones: one with America and the other locally, moving between the three recipients with change of voice and information, but like a chess master with no loss of contact, and at the same he had been listening to his secretary. Moreover, what a computer could never do, the more complex became the input and the decision required from him, the broader, the brasher, became his smile. How was he now reacting to his emissary's news? He was reacting with a most friendly sparkle. A dangerous sparkle it well could be.

Robert had not yet appeared this evening but was certain to come, Maurice was saying. He, all the while, was watching his uncle and Raoul, and he was quietly extracting from me what I knew of the village sequence. "We shall see fireworks if Robert is difficult. The Sheik is lining us up today. That's why we're here. There can be no defaulters. I suppose you have heard about the bomb. . . ."

"Just now, your father. . . ."

"Yes, it blew up a warehouse. But tomorrow they could blow up the office. We have to adopt an extreme position."

"Against the Muslims?"

"Good God, are you crazy!" He smiled. He could not see that I had made a slip and was, in any case, slower witted than he. (Always this pause with the Lebanese while they waited for you to catch up with them.) He assumed I had been teasing or perhaps indicating some subtle repercussion a month ahead. This satisfied him. He went on talking.

Best, in this company, just to listen and learn.

Over orange-flavored coffee and *baklava*, cousin Farid's voice grew louder. Till now it had chatted with the others, unctuous like the unctuous smile concealing his usual mailed fist of a face, for he happened to be sitting next to a lady. But something must have irked him, or his sense of timing could have prompted him to seize the moment—before the real business of the evening began—for suddenly his words rasped out, and his expression was that of an agitator, his very long index finger cocked in emphasis. "Do we take our orders from the Mufti? You say he has declared a Holy War, but is that also holy for a Christian? Is Our Lord involved? Where stands the Patriarch? Where stand the Christians of Egypt and Syria, relegated by Nasser and the Baathists to the rank of second class citizens? Is this our war? Must we follow those who in their hearts are traitors to Lebanon, who would surrender us to Muslim overlordship? What does Michel Chiha tell us? Are we Arabs . . . or are we Lebanese, Phoenicians? Let us stand for our citadel of freedom! We are the beacon of Christianity in Asia. All the Christians of Asia watch and pray for us in this Muslim sea. Who is this Nasser? A desperate man. A *kabūs*, a nightmare darkening our lives! Are we afraid? Are we afraid?"

He had begun rapidly, question following question out of long practice tumbling forth, till he had declared for the beacon of Christianity. And then he had slowed, his face shining and his eyes fixed on Nassib's wife, so that one suddenly guessed one channel of his influence, which would be denied to him later in the all-male conference, and there was something of his well-known press smile, of the avenging angel at a humane moment, that accompanied his articles in local magazines.

One realized: if he were a businessman, it was only because all the family were in business. And just as his own father had migrated from the office to the boudoirs of Parisian girls, so he—putting aside for the moment all his early São Paulo venture, and his failed marriage, and his trek back home—was migrating daily, at every opportunity, into the melee of the political scene; not, however, as Nassib was a part of it, with responsibility for working the show, and so obliged to bargain continuously with those classified as opponents, but as a militant extremist, a Christian commando ever ready to wield his pen or one of those machine guns he kept at his factory, until, for he was a romantic fellow, the moment might come to give his life halting the Muslims at a street barricade. He was fairly influential in the Kataeb, the Falangist party of Pierre Gemayel, and he was tolerated by the practical Hadiris. Their most colorful member. Who knew no limits. Who was now continuing: "Who planted the bomb this very day against us? Was it the Jews? Is it the Jews who threaten our bread here in Lebanon? Some say so!" He smiled scornfully. "I ask you, who is the enemy? The Communist? The Arab Nationalist? The Nasserite? Or the Jew? As a true Lebanese, as—"

"Yes, dear cousin," interrupted Raoul, "but we are solidly for the Palestinians. Many of the refugees are Christian. . . ."

These words sufficed to break the spell. Cousin Farid always did cast a spell. But now several voices came in quickly and Farid, surprised, like a netted animal, struggled and then fell silent. He cast a beady look at Raoul, who could hardly have spoken from deep conviction, but who, placed beside the Sheik, must have sensed that somebody had to stop the speech. These things had a way of getting around. General talk resumed. Maurice whispered—in between sentences flashed to other people—"Our best friends, after all, are Kuwaitis! And Saudis. We are hand in glove with Muslims!"

It was a corrective thought. The alignments of power did not necessarily oppose the religions. The sectarian challenge was often a front behind which, as from time immemorial, the conservatives ganged up together against the encroachments of the revolutionaries. Rich Maronite merchants and rich Kuwaitis (or, on the local stage, rich Sunni Beirutis) knew who their common challenger was. But for public consumption they rarely said so.

Not with bombs and knives in play.

Furthermore, concerning the Israelis, it was the greatest folly to deviate there.

Shortly after this episode the men withdrew. For Robert

had arrived at last, looking very serious and dejected, wholly taken up with the threat of the almost certain war to the plans he was launching. And because he was the one Hadiri who simply, rationally, without mystification, always said what was on his mind, he said now to the smiling family (smiling, perhaps, at his just having missed cousin Farid's panegyrics: that would certainly have stung him to a violent reply), "It's terrible, no? The old wounds are reopening. You merchants and politicians may profit, but I am working for a new society. An integrated, and secular society"—his seriousness took their smiles away—"but a crisis hardens the old divisions among the Lebanese. I have never seen so many frightened people."

"They will be more frightened after Nasser's victory." It was the Sheik's voice, slow, weighed. All became attentive. They knew he was giving, whatever his private thoughts might be, the beginning of some announcement to them. He determined the family line. He continued to Robert, "I am happy you are with us. You are my eldest son. I need your guidance. I shall surprise you with the strength of my support for your anxieties. Shall we sit in my room?"

Not a word about the elder. Not a word of reproach. Not a word about the promise that Raoul had given as his emissary to the village. That, once known, would mean a battle with Robert.

But the Sheik was an extremely far-sighted man.

And foxy, and patient, and, withal, gentle.

So the men withdrew, and I, as a visitor, though one the Sheik was feeding with a viewpoint, was left conversing with the old lady. Leila and the younger Madame Hadiri and the other two sat down to cards. To calm their nerves. The over-arching crisis was best met by a flutter at bridge. The cool evening winds played round us. The reds and blues and yellows of the carpets glowed against the high white walls. The fountain below splashed unceasingly, and from the mountain roads came the hum of traffic still wending back to the city. Cicadas. A near stillness in corners. What a wonderful summer retreat this was in which to brood, shed a skin or two, savoring the unsought sweetness of life. What a moment, though, in actuality.

How the men debated I never was to learn. (When days later I was to question Raoul, his mood by then had so corrosively altered.) However, at once, their conclusions were public. All the things the Sheik had been saying for weeks in support of the Arabs, in support of Lebanon marching beside her Muslim brothers, were re-emphasized and now magnified (To make sure of no more bomb attacks? To placate Robert's Arab Nationalist sympathies? To outdo all the other propagandists?) by a truly astonishing statement for a Maronite. It was at once dispatched to town by Maurice, to be certain of tomorrow's first editions, perhaps to reach the radio tonight. It was given to the villagers and others again gathering, squatting in the dark outside the front door. It was passed to the old lady, but in muted tones, for it was, after all, a public statement.

The Sheik was calling for a preemptive strike, an Arab first strike against Israel. It must happen at once, and war be shouldered, and all efforts of the Great Powers to restrain them, to halt their righteous regaining of the land and homes belonging to the Palestinians, must be rejected. Especially America must not be listened to once this Arab crusade had begun. But—and this but was heavily repeated—only through a first strike was such a crusade possible, only through a sudden overwhelming of the enemy. A preemptive strike was the sole way to victory. Nothing less would do, and without delay. Otherwise—and this again was repeated—he, Sheik Nassib, would be disillusioned about the intentions of the Arab commanders.

A truly subtle statement. One had to cheer Nassib. I was later to learn that during the day he had been on the phone to New York, Zurich, and Riyad, to various members of his family. Several heads had nodded in agreement. But finally he must have trusted his instinct and his own last minute sense of timing.

Robert looked pleased.

Raoul looked cryptic. He was silent in the car; then, very distantly, and characteristically, he was discussing his poetry.

We barely noticed the descent to Beirut, till the wet heat again clamped on us.

2

LEBANESE SOCIETY

৻৹ৡৢ৻৹

Some Muslim Attitudes

Two Forms of Revolt

An Approach to the Clan

Father and Son

The Young Industrialist

Some Muslim Attitudes

BEIRUT in March was chilly and wet. Fog hung over the foothills. From the sky the high spine of mountains glittered with snow between the clouds. But at sea level there was nothing but rain—interminable, people were saying, that winter. The north wind blew. The foliage shivered. The sea was a dark green breaking with spume and spray on the Corniche rocks. An itinerant fresh orange juice seller huddled miserably beneath his cart, then abandoned it for the shelter of a doorway. Roads were torrents, pavements were spattered by the water wheels of the relentless traffic. The pass to Damascus, the papers noticed, was once again blocked by snow. The mountain road had collapsed; there were rifts, craters. A bus had skidded and plunged to destruction. The rain fell with a leaden thud.

Then it cleared for a while, dripping and gurgling, and the sun came through giving a sheen to the faded white and ochre buildings. It steamed a little, it was suddenly mild; it was suddenly too warm in the cafés. The pavements filled. There was diversity of dress, such as nowadays is common anywhere, but here tricked out with tribal magnificence, practical robes from hill and desert, and the blacks and whites of sectarian holiness. There was diversity of face, coloring, gait. There were several languages. Shriller sounds. There was the constant, insistent bleep of taxis. A man standing at the door of his shop or sitting at his money-changing counter would beckon and cry, "Welcome, Welcome," or run out and grip one's arm. Peddlers, bread sellers, shoeblacks competed for attention along the pavement. Policemen struck extreme attitudes. There were plenty of pretty girls about, slipping into the pretty boutiques. The pace never slackened. It trembled toward panic. At moments, idlers and the prayerful apart, those apart who were smoking their *nargilehs*, the entire city of Beirut seemed alerted to the need of catching a particular bus.

A certain frenzy underlay all.

Then, until April, the rain slammed down again. One could easily accept that this city surpassed, in annual rainfall, the city of Manchester. They were all saying that it was a terrible year, and, of course, the long, dry summer was to come. For the moment it was best to move about by car.

I was to hire a car, but in the early days I went everywhere by taxi—not a taxi taken for oneself, but a service-taxi shared with others, moving on a fixed circuit of the town. Pause on the pavement of any main street and that minute a toot would sound. A sharp-eyed driver had seen the hesitation, and, as you turned to the cab, his right index finger would flick forward from the vicinity of the wheel, inquiring if you cared to join him. If you flicked assent, if you did not refuse him with an expressive oriental nod (the opposite to a western nod in that the chin and eyebrows lift upwards, implying distaste for any form of effort), you would be squeezing in and begging pardon for the rain and the extra wetness thrust upon the others. There could be a total of three passengers behind and two beside the driver.

At once, with barely time to close the door, the cab was off, and if there remained an empty place, now, like gunmen, you joined the driver in scanning every inch of pavement. These drivers had to fill their cabs. They needed every cent against fevered competition. Rival cabs swam down beside, racing from the lights, hooting, arguing that their hoot had attracted that fare, though, sportily, if someone lacked change, from vehicle to vehicle, as they all swam forward, coins would be passed across for a note. They handed on this urgency to you. They could be softly reproachful, struck by fate; they could be violent in both word and gesture, personally insulted by the empty place, so that other cars, and pedestrians, and you, yes even you who were paying a fare, had to feel their spleen. They might try poaching from the bus queues, a move, if any policeman saw it, that brought a deafening whistle and a fine. Or, I saw it once, they would crash another car, so intolerable had become their pain. Then several policemen converged. The whole street went up in argument.

With a full taxi it was a different story. The radio would be tuned up louder. The hand flicking the gear lever through would continue upward in a gesture of triumph and would stay suspended for some seconds near where, above the windshield, a row of saints or a scroll of Koranic wisdom had been affixed. The driver grew in size, took splendid risks bringing his car first through obstacles. There was a point in Hamra district where, if late to the lights, such a driver would cut through a service station to come to the front again. There were other points where the pavement was mounted and pedestrians driven into doorways so as the better to infiltrate. Anything went in a winning mood.

By using these service-taxis it was possible to explore most quarters of the town. This was like moving between different countries: from Armenia, to Arabia, to the Maronite people, and then on to the Anglo-Saxons. Seventy to eighty percent of each community lived within its own main quarter, mingling in the Burj, the downtown square, with adjacent suqs, brothels, and banking, and mingling in the new estates up the mountain and in Ras Beirut, the most westernized quarter. One could see where the barricades would have run in the civil fighting of 1958.

And behind these lines were the separate schools, separate hospitals, separate churches—the separately formed hearing and seeing. It was a mosaic pattern. The principal loyalty, the means of self-identification, rested within the primary community.

"What are you, then? Are you Lebanese?"

"You see, my family is Armenian. We live here. My brother is in America. My other brother has returned to Russia—do you understand, to Soviet Armenia. We stay inside our history. . . ."

"Yes, yes, I follow your question. In England, of course, I would answer to people that I am Lebanese, but in myself, you know, I am still a Syrian. We are Sunni Muslims; we came from Damascus; we have lived in Beirut for a hundred years."

"Lebanese? Why yes. What else? I am a Christian—that is, I am a Catholic Christian. An Orthodox might answer you differently!"

"Lebanese? You put a difficult question. I am a Druze. We lived here first on the Mountain. I am a Druze. Hah, I am a Druze. *C'est tout!*"

And there were other variations.

Then, toward the outskirts of town were the shacks and compounds of the near-helot community, the semi-fenced-in undesirables (except as a whip to the world's conscience): the Palestinian refugees. Their lot was indeed quite separate. A few might enter the city as peddlers, office cleaners, as driftwood through the streets; by night, it was said, as thieves and assassins. A few were being trained to a trade. But the

vast majority, a hundred thousand or more, were being left
to rot, were being meagerly fed and medically controlled
and the children given primary schooling, but then left
helpless, except to breed, so that now their children and their
children's children were eating their hearts out with bitterness.

The service-taxis went still further, competing with the
buses to all regions of the country. The Burj was the great
market for travel. Turn down any of the streets leading off
it, and a man would be crying "Saida!" or "Tripoli!" or
"Baalbak!" or "Aley!" or, still further, to "Damascus!" Just
as in Damascus, with the same matter-of-factness, there were
men crying "Amman!" and "Baghdad!" It seemed sufficient
just to step inside one of these streamlined automobiles to
be swept east to India or China. And that not beyond local
enterprise.

The first, simple rule in Lebanon: show your money and
name your wish.

With the snow still blocking the country roads and giving
a breathtaking panorama each time the sun came out and one
looked across the bay to the hills, I stayed for the time being
in the city, exploring its diverse patterns and making the
acquaintance of several people. Among these was Professor
Chaamaya. I was particularly interested in the confrontation,
such a primary feature of Lebanon, between Christian and
Muslim traditions and belief. In fact I had come back to this
area, where I had spent four years of the war (my generation
means by this the war of 1939–45), to learn a little more
about Islam as the matrix of the Arab world . . . if that
were still so. Secularization, flattening every sacred thought
in Europe, might have won the game here too.

Professor Chaamaya was himself engaged in studies of this
sort, as I discovered through attending his lecture. He was
imposingly courteous, a rubicund figure with precise, beautiful
speech and a way of pausing as though we all should listen

to the greater truths proceeding from the silence. His subject was the Muslim-Christian dialogue. At last, he was saying, adherents of these faiths could meet and join search as equals. Gone was the see-saw of victor and victim that around and across the Mediterranean had embattled the last thirteen centuries. Gone were the Saracens, and gone the Mandates, and gone—and he smiled and paused because his audience was very largely Christian—was the narrower sort of missionary endeavor. Truth could be sought through neighborly tolerance. He cited Greek and Semitic sources from which both faiths had evolved. They worshipped the one God. They were equally faced with contemporary scientific rejection. They should study how they could enrich each other, as, above all, Massignon had taught. This could not be left to theologians.

His audience was well-groomed, attentive. They listened keenly when, addressing Islam, he called for a revitalized Koran, with the aid of modern critical techniques. He deplored the weight of Sunni dogma. He asked Muslims to study the Cross for the essence that the Christian heart found there, and not as they had viewed it centuries ago.

To Christianity once again he pleaded that the gifts of Islam should not be equated with the seeming backwardness of the present. In its great age Islamic culture had raised up the West; it still had genius. The message of Muhammad spoke freshly to men—one could look at the area of race and color; all men were directly called to respond to the power of God in their lives.

"God is most great. God is most great. I confess that there is no god but God"—he was intoning the muezzin's call to prayer—"I confess that Muhammad is the Messenger of God. Come ye to prayer. Come ye to the good. . . ."

As he spoke, the simple outlines of a mosque, with its fountains and courts and inner space for worship, took shape

as a place of eternal vitality, of no less value for mankind
than a church. And vice-versa. The way was one.

After the lecture he was surrounded by students launching
complicated arguments.

I met him next in his book-packed room at the American
University. This institution is the most modern university,
the most excellent and lively, in the entire Near East. Founded
a hundred years ago by the American missionary Daniel Bliss,
whose long-bearded, spade-shaped face looks squarely out
from corridor photographs, it accommodates over three-
thousand undergraduates, a quarter of them women; from
sixty countries (it can be added: from twenty or so different
sects); and having survived both Turkish and French overlordship, it is now contending with the propaganda of those
extreme Arab nationalists for whom nothing American can
be trusted, and whom, as often as not, the university has
educated.

A nice tug of loyalties. But so much does it give toward
the skills and mental discipline needed by the Arabs, and its
independence helped by the balance, religious and political,
of which Lebanon is composed, that it can plan not un-
reasonably for a second century. A good meeting place in a
fragmented city and in a wildly disordered area of the world;
an oasis of inquiry and eclectic reasoning, something, one
should add, as essentially of the city, in the tradition of the
Roman law schools here, as any of its less harmonious features.
An old city. An accommodating place.

It was very pleasant, among early April blossoms, the sea
shining blue and the air warm, although the mountains were
a background of snow, of snow peaks jutting out of mountain
mist (although by evening it could be raining again), to walk
about in the excitement of students, the endless capacity to
talk there shown, and to turn into a professor's study so as
to add one's own drop of inquiry.

He offered coffee, cigarettes; he began making two lists: of books I should read; of people I should meet. Students floated in; the telephone rang. The pressure was always discreet, tentative, but unless one could pursue one's talk in aphorisms, not much ground could be covered. He began, "The trouble with Islam was our Arabic tendency—not a fault we lose—always to adopt an extreme attitude in the circumstances of a particular dispute and then to build on that attitude forever. Hence the accretions of Sunni dogma, and of the *Shari'a*, the Holy Law. Much of the early Apostolic tradition, the *Hadith*, was added by doctors of the time to counter particular threats: a one-sidedness irrelevent today. You can see our need: to sift, to uncover, as Christian scholars have done for Christianity."

"Would you say that that has halted the decline of faith?"

"Oh yes." He was already turning to a student, a magnificent girl who had knocked and entered, apologetic but set on attention.

A few minutes later—"If we sift, we discover that the Koranic God is not just arbitrary, as the Christian world has portrayed Him. At times, we find that He is also a Divinity working to release moral energy in men, to produce in us creative moral attitudes."

"One rarely hears this view."

"Faced with the dogma, how can Muslims themselves get through to it? How can they hear His call freshly . . . for instance, in politics, to discuss and participate, and not to accept predetermining authority? The Koran is no book for dictatorships. Look," he said, "I am going to send you to the Mufti."

"Is he a modernist?"

"By no means. But that is where you can begin your inquiries. And then to this doctor. Please phone me this evening." He wrote his telephone number on the paper.

"Then one day you must come to tea. In my office here, look, it is hopeless." Two more eager students had entered.

The Mufti of the Lebanese Republic, at his headquarters in the Dar al-Fatwa, was a beautifully composed gentleman. We sat in a largely empty room with walls and windows reminiscent of a clinic, and against this nothingness he and his sheiks nodded and whispered into life, disputing the exact meaning of a word with the glamor of a medieval tableau. Downstairs there was a luxurious car, and a chauffeur, and secretaries, and gendarmerie, but here more of the timeless moment, as faced with the conundrum of a word like "insight," the good doctors clucked together. They had been asking for an explanation of Quakerism, a reversal of the intention of the interview, but from that ground we progressed rapidly.

Much of the talk was lost in cliché (when one thinks about it afterward), but orthodoxy did come through from this spokesman of the Sunni community. He attacked the secular trend in Syria; he praised Nasser as a good Muslim, as a man whose heart was open to the poor. Here in Lebanon, from his point of view, one could live with the Christians in brotherly love, yet, overall, Lebanon's future must increasingly fall within the Muslim sphere in fulfillment of Islamic precepts. There should be no intermarriage with Christians. He found it abhorrent that a Muslim girl should ever wish to marry a Christian.

He and the ample-robed men about him kept to this point for some time.

Then, asked about the interchange of ideas (as between Muslims and Christians), he replied that sufficient truth had been revealed, infallibly and forever, through the books of the Prophet. Holy Writ needed careful understanding, but it was the task of the doctors to give this. On them good Muslims still depended.

Asked about the welfare of children whose parents could not afford their schooling (that neighborhood was teeming with urchins, barefoot, out of tenements and hovels), the Mufti replied that education began with the Five Pillars of Islam. To teach these to his child was the parent's duty. These, because they produced good Muslims, were the basic education.

Well, such interviews tell little, as equally the next one granted to me, except that in a field where reformers are active there must also be conservatives. Their debate might be one for a hundred years, as for the last century it had been in Christendom.

But on returning to my room, I looked up the Five Pillars to see what children of the poor should rely on. The first Pillar was the credal confession: There is no god but God, and Muhammad is His Prophet. The second Pillar was the recital of prayer each dawn, noon, afternoon, and sunset, and again before retiring. Each of these would be spoken confessions accompanied by ritual movements of the body, including two full prostrations—a vignette, in memory, of all Arabs praying, whether in mosque or in the desert, on beaches among the holiday crowds, or in the seclusion of their balconies; wherever they could spread their mats and face Mecca in absolute submission. The third Pillar was the requirement of fasting, especially during Ramadan. The fourth Pillar was the giving of alms, the giving of all that was not essential to oneself and family back to the community. The fifth Pillar was the pilgrimage to Mecca.

I returned to the Professor for more information. What other attitudes existed?

He received me at home, in another Muslim district, rich and poor again jumbled together, his own elegant block of apartments (literally, for his family owned it) rising out of the patchwork of shops, two-story passage and courtyard

housing, workshops, storerooms, connecting alleys, hawkers'
barrows, rubbish dumps, all astir with cries and the clang
inseparable from a corner of the Orient. It had not been
easy to find the place. Street names had been abolished in
Beirut and a weird system of numbers substituted. My driver
was a Christian Arab from Haifa, not too happy at entering
the quarter. His requests for help had been most aggressive.
Two infidels here, we had been sent in circles.

Then the Chaamaya building appeared. On entering the
lift, quiet returned.

He mentioned that his wife was in Tripoli with her family.
A squint-eyed servant had shown me in, a suspicious fellow
who hung about as if I had come to brain his master. He
was sent off to prepare the tea. A tall son entered, bowed,
disappeared. All the corridors were lined with books. We
passed by a salon filled with flowers and went into the
Professor's study. Here, one could see, was his home within
a home. There was a good Seljuk rug on the floor, tables
with mother-of-pearl inlay, bowls and ewers of cobalt blue
decorated with floral scrolls. On a shelf below books, on a
dark brocade, were pocket-size Korans in gold-tooled leather
and with illuminated pages. A motif there, repeated on the
bowls, appeared again in the Professor's buttonhole. He was
a dandified person, and he sported a geranium.

He showed the Korans, then dismissed his collection. As a
younger man he had deplored the break-up of the Ottoman
Empire. All his brothers had hailed independence only to see
it surrendered to the French. He had looked back with
nostalgia to the greatest Muslim Empire in history. So,
naturally, he had collected mementos. From his father he
had inherited others. He would like to tell me that so fierce
had been his opposition to the French Mandate—he had been
jailed twice for his part in disorders—that, though never a
member of the Party, he had worked with Communists

and given them shelter. He had also fooled British Intelligence.

All that was past. From law and philosophy he had turned to the field of comparative religion. What a field lay there for a Muslim scholar! How necessary were such studies in Lebanon. Although it was true that clan interests exploited and exacerbated the confessional divisions—as had the Turks, then the Great Powers, seeking advantage in the nineteenth century—it was also true that the division was there. The Christians of Lebanon still believed that the Muslims, if they could, would islamize Lebanon; the Muslims here still felt it a shame to be ruled over by a Christian President. Much ignorance entered into this. Antipathy. Fear. Centuries of fighting. Propaganda from vested interests. How necessary to open the doors to Muslim-Christian understanding. Where better to begin than at the heart of their faiths, showing how these ran parallel?

"So you will approve also of Christian-Muslim marriages? Shouldn't the personal status law, which governs marriage, divorce, and so on, be immediately secularized? At the moment here ecclesiastical writ, practically speaking, stands more in the way of young intermarriageable couples than creeds perhaps that they no longer stick to. So I gather from students."

A rather lengthy silence. Professor Chaamaya, beneath his courtesy and his practical idealism, retained, perhaps from his Ottoman period, a discreetly seignorial mien. He had been born into an old established family that had held high office under the Porte; and at other moments, in other company, the fact that he was a Muslim might come first.

"Yes, eventually it follows. Yes. At the University cases are arising. If they have to marry they go over to Cyprus. It is best, perhaps, if the man is Muslim." He hesitated. "There are family difficulties. Even where faith has gone, one's community remains, psychologically, one's world. Young people break out, then feel their isolation. Possibly study, my type of research; more of that should come first. But yes, the personal status law should be secularized. This has already happened in Egypt. Here, don't forget, you have also to convert the entrenched Christian Establishment!" Smiling, feeling that he had retrieved his position, he leaned forward and poured the tea.

He began to show, through slight indications, that his own faith had been influenced by Sufism. He had Sufi texts in English translation. I remarked on this, and he began saying again that a new moral impulse, a feeling of heart, was needed among the orthodox Sunnis. He did not hold with breakaway sects like, here in Lebanon, the Shia and the Druzes. Rather he would seek to reconcile them by opening up the Koran afresh. All moods, all impulses could be found there. As in Christian prayer. In an agnostic world men of faith should draw together.

He pulled down a book of Sufi poems and suggested that I might like to read one to him. I didn't mind. This was better than in Finland where the Bishop of Tampere, after tea and cakes, had bid me recite the Lord's Prayer.

But I had barely begun, from FitzGerald's translation of the Speech of Birds by the Persian mystic 'Attar . . .

"Then cried the Spokesman, 'be it even so:
Let us but see the Fount from which we flow,
And, seeing, lose Ourselves therein!' And, lo!
Before the Word was utter'd, or the Tongue
Of Fire replied, or Portal open flung,
They were within—"

when the door burst open and a child came in, followed by a lady of gentle, middle years.

The child, his youngest son, kissed his hand. The lady was his sister, Mrs. Najla Zoghal.

We talked for some minutes. When I learned her husband's name, I mentioned that I assiduously read his editorials in a translation that I was able to come by. "You must meet him then. He is pro-British. He is determined to see the best in everyone! I can't think what he will do to Lebanon."

The Professor explained that his brother-in-law, the journalist Dr. Hamid Zoghal, worked, like himself, for Muslim-Christian understanding, but purely on the secular, political level. "He is an atheist according to our friend the Mufti! He prefers to sweep all religions away."

"No, Sleiman, I think you are not being fair." Her tone was aggrieved, though still sweetly polite. Her languid eyes were brightly defensive. Then she seemed to apologize for this emotion. In the aftermath she told her brother to bring me later in the week to her house.

The Zoghals lived in a two-story house behind a high garden wall. A servant came to open the gate, watched by a second servant from the terrace. It was wet and windy, and the bamboos swished, and the stone pines and a fig tree waved above a marble pool and fountain. It looked desolate, but sprigs of blossom and the burgeoning of the bougainvillea and jacaranda and Judas trees and bowls planted with mimosa and cyclamen and the trailing of honeysuckle from the terrace promised, once the summer broke in, a close, heavily perfumed garden, a private arbor in the midst of the city.

The hall was dark. Then the sitting room, with windows opening onto the terrace, was rich with carpets, settees, and cushions, and the walls were closely covered with paintings and vitrines for some late Turkish glassware. There was a proliferation of small tables and lamps. It was evening after dinner; this sort of gathering to gossip and argue was called a *sahra*, a little *sahra* as dinner was excluded—an old feature of Beiruti life. Mrs. Zoghal wore a *jellābah*, a long, wide-sleeved, embroidered gown that recalled tented Arabian splendor, while her sister, a tall, distracted woman, wore the latest of trouser suits.

Najla Zoghal was petite and chubby, warm-eyed, languid in voice, used, one would say, to pleasing and to listening and to flattering people with an ever ready chuckle. Her husband had been delayed at his office. She lingeringly made the introductions, as though with her warmth she could cement new ties. She settled on the cushions as though all her life had been a sweet nostalgic existence, a harem existence debating trivia; then belied this as she turned from her sister and another woman and their talk of maids and came into the main discussion with quiet words showing strength of character. Her son Ali, tall and fiery, stood protectively by her couch; and the scorn with which he was pleased to talk hung about his face all the time.

Central to the occasion was another man, whom they called Fawzi, also a journalist but a Palestinian who now lived and worked in Beirut and who spoke only English apart from Arabic. They had probably been speaking Arabic earlier, before I arrived with Professor Chaamaya and, on our heels, an American professor. But one could not know this from the ease with which they were now using the English language. Ali attended the American University. Najla's sister had lived in America with her former husband, a diplomat. They had all traveled, with the exception of Fawzi, who had only been to Cairo and Damascus. And as children of an old governing family, with plenty of Turkish blood mixed in, they would have grown up with an armory of languages.

The journalist Fawzi had a guarded face, a stubby moustache, a fuzz of hair. His opinions were evidently all embittered, and he nagged at one with unfriendly questions. Then suddenly out of a pause, as with a lighthouse beam revolving, out came an explosion of venom revealing a white heat inside. Then he was silent again and a shade darker.

"Are you an orientalist?" he first asked me.

"No."

"The western orientalists describe only what is dead in our society. Dead and past. They like to feed on it. They feed each other"—his tone was harshening as he came out with this unfair view—"they come thousands of miles in pursuit of necrophily! But the Arabs today should be defined in terms of the future wrestling to break out of them. Are you a tourist?" There was a shade of spite.

"I used to live in the Middle East. A return visit."

"You should have chosen July, for the Baalbak Festival! You would have been taken also to Bayt al-Din, the Cedars, the Casino, to several night clubs, then forwarded to Holy Jerusalem!" Pause. He spat out, "We are not proud of this society. Lebanon is a sick growth." Pause. "Are you staying at the Phoenicia Hotel?"

I disclaimed such affluence and mentioned to him the modest address at which I was residing. He was not won over.

"It is a question of time. We shall outflank these Christians who lord it over us, who profited from the French Mandate to climb on the necks of everyone else—"

"How Lebanese you sound, Fawzi!" It was Najla's sister. "You remind me of the song, 'Ma hala, ma hala, gatl en Nasara . . . how sweet, how sweet, to kill the Christians!' It comes of writing Beirut editorials for our friend the Gentleman in Cairo!"

He shrugged, annoyed. "The Arab world is one. Or it will be when we have reconquered Palestine. Who else but Nasser should give us leadership?"

"Maybe. He is a useful bogeyman—for the Maronites! It helps to restrain them."

Najla: "He has moved too far to the left. He let all the Marxists out of prison." There was a laugh. "Like Fawzi. Fawzi, is it true, that in prison with you in Cairo there was a Russian, an American, a Saudi Arabian, and a Jew, all suffering the Rayyis' displeasure?"

"I was never in prison." He disliked the humor. "I was very impressed by my year in Egypt. Nasser one day will unite us all and lead us to our Arab socialist society."

In the pause, noticeably skeptical, I asked him, "Will that be an Islamic society or a more secularized one?"

"A secular society, though religion has its uses in helping to guide and to rally people." He gave his slightly spiteful smile. "We could never progress in the harness of Islam."

"So Hamid says, but my brother thinks the opposite." Najla looked for support to Chaamaya. "For me, my whole outlook stays Muslim, I find, even when I am shopping in Paris!"

Her brother refused to enter this discussion.

It was at this point that Ali joined in. He turned from the couch with a gesture of impatience and of arrogance; then he wheeled on Fawzi: "I was asking you before! You never answered my question. Who is Nasser to desert his brethren? He acts with contempt. Is that leadership?"

"He acts with wisdom. Am I not the Palestinian? Is it not I who have seen my family fleeing from land that they have held for centuries and seen the house in which I was born stolen by a Jew? I tell you, Ali"—Fawzi's emotion was now so impregnated with pain that it was purified of its former unpleasantness—"that these so-called Hebrews who claim their Promised Land have less ancient Hebrew blood than I! They have Slav, Turkoman, German blood, and habits and mentality, from their so-called Diaspora. Two millennia ago some of their kindred held a partial dominion in Palestine, but what title does that give them now? A title to root us out like weeds? Are we in turn to reclaim Spain, where we ruled for nine hundred years?" He paused, astray, as so often with Arabs, in the convolutions of his own eloquence, quite evidently much of it for the room at large.

He remembered swiftly: "My father defied the British Mandate for thirty years in Palestine. We were never taken in by the Zionists or by the imperialist strategy that became their willing accomplice. Do you think that I would falter now if this was the moment to retake my country? Nasser has wisdom. Your friends are precipitate. War there must be, but when we are ready."

He was flushed and darkly seething with hatred, but also with satisfaction at his argument. In a moment the whole company was debating it, as became apparent it had been debating before: in a word, whether the latest incident, near Galilee, with the Syrians losing six MIG fighters through Israeli action, should be escalated or should lead to prudence. Nasser, patently, had opted for prudence. As Chaamaya said, with the nonchalance of one who had once been a militant, "Wait a year, and the Egyptians will have learned how to fly these Sukhoy 7's. It is common knowledge that they don't know now. A year is enough. But the Syrians have always been the most impatient of Arabs."

"Uncle!" Ali, pale and haughty but studiously polite, was divided as to whom he should tackle. He said, "Time also works for the enemy! At least we cannot leave him to consolidate." Then he was turning more to Fawzi again, edging him back to the wall, thrusting, "Nasser will always betray the Arabs. He is an aging man. He is a balloon of words. Rather than strike he will give out warnings! It is Al Fatah that suits our mood . . . the nightly strike against Jewish installations . . . the terror to hurt till their foreign backers and their immigrants and their thieving sabras cannot stand the nightmare longer! Then they will leave, or accept our terms."

"Will they leave?" queried Najla. Sweetly, from her cushions, she admired her son. He was the dashing horseman raider.

He had silenced Fawzi's attempt to reply, by continuing: "We have gained self-respect. We no longer wait for the politicians. *Al 'izzah wa'l-karamah wa'l majd!* How else can your own Palestinians, as the years go by, remember their country, even though they have to tread it at night? It is honorable of the Syrians to assist them. Fawzi, do you know what the girl students are saying in the University canteen: 'Why aren't you boys out with Al Fatah? Are you scared to kill the Jews?' Can one answer by quoting Nasser!"

Later, when I had a word with Ali, difficult to come by as he distrusted westerners, he amplified, "I should like to go over one dark night into occupied Palestine and kill ten Jewish women and their children. To kill them, if that would send the balloon up!"

"But what if you lose the war that would follow?"

He looked me over with extreme distaste.

His aunt, Najla's sister, was saying, "Sooner or later we must get rid of those Jews. I feel that they would be much happier in America. Herzl was the cause of all this trouble, living as he did in imperialist times. It was quite normal to colonize then. But why is it we who have to pay this price of western Europe's guilty conscience? It is revolting. It is something obscene that you have done to us! You will thank us one day for persisting against Israel; for then you will have to face yourselves! It's strange, your love-hate for the Jews."

"I thought that the English were always supposed to have had a love-hate for the Arabs."

"Oh, the English! Who knows what they feel." She was drinking whiskey, looking very elegant in her sailor-cut trouser suit. The lines in her face were fading away with the heat of the all-absorbing topic. Israel, in many ways for Arabs, was an externalizing catalyst.

Ali was again holding the floor: "Precisely to this day nineteen years ago, in April, 1948, the Irgun entered Deir Yassin and massacred Arab women and children. There were two hundred and fifty of them! That was a way to create panic. That helped them to win the war that they started a month later. It showed that terror pays. As Begin boasted, 'We entered Haifa like a knife into butter.' Is it surprising that there were refugees! Are we not morally justified, Uncle, in using the same methods against them? Thieves and murderers and hypocrites; don't they all deserve to die now?"

As he was speaking, another man entered, tall as he, broader, the face largely disguised by dark glasses; but the father obviously, his hand calmly, deftly, for an instant touching Ali's shoulder. Then he saluted Chaamaya; he was moving to Najla, already on her feet, her hand extending to give his arm an affectionate press. A warm, courteous personality, with a deft, sly appraisal of the atmosphere into which he was coming. By his walk, his clothes, his manner one would judge him to be a rather romantic figure.

"Good evening!" Introduced, he was rapidly telling me, with zest and informality, that as Chaamaya had told him of my interest in Islam, there were a number of people he would like me to meet, but, frankly, practical people, people working on practical issues, which, if there was to be a future for anyone—let alone Koranic scholars!—had to be solved here in Lebanon. In Lebanon. Yes. He was not, like his family, lost in the Panarab mists! He did not wait for Greater Syria solutions. He was a friend of the Lebanese Christians because

he was working for a sound local evolution, and there was
no other practical course.

"No," he was saying firmly to Ali, "I don't think these
raids should be encouraged. *Karr u farr*—that's the Bedouin
method, but not one for a country like ours whose progress
depends on the temperature being kept low. First things first.
For us Lebanon remains the important nut to crack. My
son . . ."

His son, blazing, but silenced by the fact that it was the
parent speaking, only muttered, "Damascus speaks differently.
Their radio promises even fiercer raids."

And Najla's sister: "I sometimes think that you would
support a deal with Israel, Hamid. Just like a Maronite banker.
But surely for us the overwhelming issue is that of the
refugees?"

He was very patient: "If each of our countries puts its
own house in order, we can absorb, if necessary, the refugees
—or, yes, wait, we can confront Israel with real power which
is economic and not a toy cupboardful of missiles. I support
Nasser's achievements at home; I dislike his squandering of
energy abroad. In Yemen, for instance. First things first. Then
the problems by themselves diminished."

The women shrugged. The professors nodded. The son
burned with indignation. But Dr. Hamid had already stepped
aside, his arm alighting on Fawzi's shoulder, drawing him,
half whispering, to a corner.

The party at this stage broke up into a collection of
low-voiced exchanges. Talking to the American, I thought
further of our host, and I recalled his glowing editorials in
which indeed he praised Nasser, but always against a telling
catalog of all that remained to be done in Egypt. Subtly he
cut Nasser down to size.

Equally, concerning Lebanon, he conveyed the usual

Muslim resentment and envy of the all-pervasive Christian predominance. He fulminated against Christian wealth flaunted in the eyes of the poor. He was a teaser out of their financial practices. Yet, against this, he hailed the reformers—within the bureaucracy, among intellectuals—who were calling for constitutional changes to get beyond the political impasse; and he acknowledged that most of these were Christians. Very subtly he labeled Muslims as equally people who must examine their position. The only future was supra-confessional.

He never directly attacked Nasser's power spilling over, as it did, into Lebanon. But what he did do, again and again, was to call for a local leader of stature. He had supported General Fuad Shihab in the years following 1958. Now he seemed to be saying to his readers, haven't we such a one among the Muslims?

Along such lines Nasser faded out.

And from day to day he was a great crusader, especially each Friday when he addressed himself to a faulty sector of national life. It would be roads, or agricultural development, or tax collection, or education. He consistently fought the political set-up as one which devalued every issue. His style was inclined to be over-eloquent—at the conclusion it was tactfully vapid—but in between, hard punches were delivered. One naturally wanted to question him further.

His way was to make this seem very easy. "Of course . . . you will come to see me in my office. I will give you a list of people to meet. We will discuss. I will explain. I have a villa near Aley. We could run up there for a quieter discussion." Even in the house, since his return, the telephone had kept on ringing.

He said, eyeing the company about him, "The old Islamic order of society has gone for good, yet, mentally, Muslims behave as if it were still protecting them. No wonder our Christian friends are confused and fear that it can still drag

them under. There is an immense task, of education—of
communication, as Americans term it. One factor, of course,
about Israel is that she is speeding up our ability to learn."
He glanced around to where his son was still fuming, seeking
consolation with Najla. He grinned cheerfully.

"Come to see me tomorrow. Come, say, about four to the
office." He was off to have a pressing word with Chaamaya.

Next day, it so happened, I kept the appointment, only
to be gently told by his secretary that Dr. Zoghal had flown
to Amman but would return next day. Could I ring him then?

I rang the next day, but by then Dr. Zoghal had flown
off to a conference in Rome. He would return in two days.
Could I ring once more?

I rang three or four days later, but by then Dr. Zoghal
had gone to London. "He hasn't forgotten you," cried the
secretary, and I assumed that she was just being sympathetic;
but then she continued, "He asked me to make an appointment
for you with Dr. Hadiri. He said it should be most important
for you." She explained who this new gentleman was—and
so put me in touch with Robert Hadiri, the oldest son of
Sheik Nassib; in fact opened the door (and from an impulse
coming from her boss's brain a whole continent away) to
the very heart of my Lebanese experience, most of it to take
place among Maronites.

But that, I was to find, was a typical gift from this
generous-hearted and subtle Muslim.

That first evening his idealism, though it earned him teasing
from his sister-in-law, continued to spread about the room,
subduing anything contrary. As the American said, "Give
him twenty years, and maybe people here will amend the
Constitution. They'll want to, just to have one Muslim
President!" That was the kind of comment he drew. So long
as he was there. A charismatic charm.

We broke up late. It was raining again. The city of Beirut,

with its pullulating needs, so many of them tugging in different directions, for the most part appeared to be sleeping. A few service-taxis were still on their circuits. The Burj blazed, and the cabaret quarter. But most of the apartment lights were dimmed. This was also an early-rising city.

Two Forms of Revolt

Old Testament poets and prophets were forever praising the smell of Lebanon. One can picture them hiking down the coast in spring or kicking gently along on an ass. Fountains, orchards, streams gladdened them; they tasted the wine and the spicy food, then rested in the shade of a pomegranate tree. Today one remarks on the apple blossom, and the thick, glistening clusters of orange, and the river valleys planted with banana and grapefruit and sweet lemons, and, taller on the skyline, the eucalyptus, and the beachside palm, then pines, poplars. But one scene overlays the other, and the brilliant morning air is the same, and the spray-wet earth, and the blue of the sea and fleecy sky tilting at the mountains, high to one's right as one speeds north up basically the same road as the Romans lay from Antioch to Acre.

What is purely modern are the advertisements, wall-size, from grove and cliff, and the sludge of food cans on the shore, and, as an ancient prophet would see it, the God-denying ways of the traffic.

It was difficult, in a service-taxi, up the coast road from Beirut to Tripoli, to take in much more than the traffic. Five passengers squeezed with the driver into garlic-laced proximity. On one side I had a turbaned gentleman thumbing his ninety-nine prayer beads, on the other, a dainty Armenian lady who recoiled each time the antics of the taxi sent me pressing against her. In front two lads, intoning with the radio, appeared actually to be inciting the driver to improve on his hitherto best speed. Never, despite oncoming automobiles and trucks in our path and the occasional figure of a portly villager or risk-running child trying to cross, did we brake. We might coast for seconds, but this particular taxi seemed to have reserves of acceleration never before known to man; so our usual response was to step on the gas. We stepped on it, naturally, down the straight, through villages and across the railway line that twined about our entire route, and we rip-roared round corners. At one moment we were deliberately passing another car itself in the process of passing another car—all this on a right-angle corner, the insult of these rivals' presence, the need to slap them down, proving too heady for our hero driver, himself from time to time demoted by the latest Citroën or Jaguar. Life is the acceptance of risk, say philosophers, adding, if they are Muslim philosophers, "Nothing can befall us but what God hath destined; and, God will mislead whom He pleaseth." He was very actively misleading our chauffeur.

But He had other plans, it would seem, for us. We came through. We were not in the statistics, themselves a daily average and available by evening, of three collisions, two men dead, and eleven injured taken off to hospital.

What other impressions along this route filtered through one's tingling nerves? I cannot speak of Jbail (Byblus) because our view of it was a market street with a bus swinging away from our hood and a policeman angrily blowing his whistle. In order to stop us? No, to hasten on the traffic.

There were mountains all the way, the snow receding before the bouts of hot spring sun. A number of villages were

beflagged and beflowered, the red anemone especially showing; animals were decked with blue beads, with red henna
smudged on their foreheads; even bicycles were dressed for
celebration. Some festival was in the offing, and the cafés
were boisterous. A parade of children halted to let our
demented taxi pass.

One recalled that this was a myth-drenched littoral, the
figures of Astarte and Adonis dancing their priapic dance for
the season of crops, celebrating the return of the god from
his winter exile under the earth. As in Greece, no doubt,
the living at this season would feel very close to the dead,
a single community linked to the soil; and shrines, tombs,
and sacred wells and trees would be centers of joy and pagan
pleading. Even the Romans had noticed this love of the
coastal Syrians for their spring celebrations as especially
debauched, even in their eyes; had noticed, too, before
Christianity, then Islam, had multiplied doctrines, the extreme
fragmentation of the people, each district with its cult and
temple—just as later they recorded, when "Syrian merchants"
were living and flourishing throughout the Roman Empire,
their passionate addiction to the Cross of Jesus. Cult, blood-
warm passion, individualism—these also went to any present
view of them.

Mamluk guard towers on promontories, fragments of
Crusader chapels, Ayyubid outposts—one's eye flicked to
them and beyond them to the postcard sea and the rocky
shore and the figure of a shepherd, and, beyond him, to a
flight of gulls or inland to the hills. Then back to the road.

No matter, for Tripoli lay ahead, still something of a
Mamluk city on guard against Frankish designs. I had spent
a leave there during the war, after the Vichy capitulation.
A city with a hilltop Crusader castle, ruined yet splendid in
silhouette, and, as with its other Crusader remnants, occasional
doorway, column, inscription, and, most strikingly, the

Lombard tower kept as minaret for the Great Mosque. The castle had been blended into the honeycomb of suqs and mosques and baths and scholarly *madrasahs* that made up the new Arab city once the Crusaders had been put to flight. Around this had been built gardens and aqueducts famous through the East. A good-living city, a bastion of Islam, always with a critical eye on the Christians. In modern times, in 1958, the challenge to President Camille Chamoun broke into open fighting here, leading to that summer's civil war. His chief opponent, subsequently to become Prime Minister and to hold that office during most of the years since then, was Rashid Karrami, of a family of muftis, the unquestioned leader of Muslim Tripoli.

With a final spurt down the boulevard cutting across a modern suburb, we arrived; not actually ahead of schedule. Pulp from the road. It was a miracle to walk.

I was seeking out a gentleman, a friend, perhaps a relative on his wife's side, of Professor Chaamaya. He was a learned doctor. By following the suq from the Great Mosque to Khan al-Saboun, then inquiring there, I should be shown his store. He was a cloth merchant. His sons and brothers ran the business, and he mostly attended to his prayers. The professor described him as a good man.

I loitered on the way, with each footstep feeling some return of the solid earth. I entered the mosque for a moment's quiet. There was a devotee praying at the front of the space facing the *muhrab*, or niche, by the pulpit, which marked the direction of Mecca. It was not a stipulated hour for prayer, so he must have had some further reason. He had already begun the sequence of movements that form a complete prayer, or *rak'a*. His head was bowed, his body inclined so that his hands could rest upon his knees. Then he was upright. Then there followed a prostration so absolute, with his toes, knees, hands, and forehead thrust upon the floor, that unless this pointed to a private anxiety bringing him at this hour to the mosque, the silence of the courtyards wafting about us, the carpets running with color in the sun that shone obliquely between the pillars, then it must point to the general impulse behind this whole ritual of Islam, the utter submission to unknown forces holding life and death in their palm. The fear of offending them. The eagerness to praise them. The gratitude for the easement of soul promised to him who sincerely listened to their messenger Muhammad.

A primitive but deeply satisfying process. A Muslim at prayer tells one something about our universal nature; he probes where reason too glibly withholds us. He cleanses, frees himself of guilt. The dark turns light. He emerges unified at that particular level.

The *rak‘a* continued, in a kneeling position, hands on knees, the trunk upright. At this point, following the prostration, he would be asking for protection and for mercy. A further prostration, and then he was standing. And then it was all beginning again, the hands flanking the ears to accompany the first confession, "God is most great."

As I arose from squatting on the carpet, *Guide Bleu* in hand, another worshipper entered and asked me in the sweetest manner, "Have you been studying the Holy Book, sir?"

"No, sir, not the Holy Book, yet a helpful book," was the most I could give him.

He nodded satisfaction.

I continued down the suq, stopping once or twice where the manner and call of a particular merchant promised pleasant conversation. Where in the West we battle through crowds, metal basket in hand, from shelf to shelf, and then to the till and then back home, in an eastern suq one looks for conversation. Of course one buys, but the context is different. The variability of price alone encourages study of the other person. The atmosphere is far more polite. And then above all it is a moment, like another, when this or that idea can be enlarged on. Time is required? But we all have time, time for the suq or time for television.

Chaamaya's friend was a whiskery old fellow with the cherubic smile I was beginning to associate with Muslims of his age in Tripoli. His store was commodious, stacked with cloths that, bolt by bolt, the salesmen were unfurling for the ladies: brilliant silks flecked with silver that were being pawed and, so it seemed, rejected as too commonplace by ladies shrouded for their outing in long black veils. Their noses showed like bandits' noses when they have pulled the nylon stocking over. Their eyes flickered darkly beneath.

The learned doctor led me upstairs to a single room without decoration, but with a hookah ready for lighting and smoking. With coffee brought by one of his sons we ate molasses made from grapes. It was clear, spiritually, that he lived *dans le vrai*, like those men glimpsed in the mosque, secured by faith and a natural humility. That he fell back on Koranic quotations and a repeated *"Bismillâh"* and *"Al-hamdu lillâh"* and *"Inshâ'llâh"* and *"Allâhu akbar"* when asked just anything was no matter. His serenity provided sufficient answer. His will had been handed over to his master, and his master bade him be sweet and simple.

This good nature extended even, some half hour later, to the entry of a nephew who was of an opposite disposition. This young man was a student in Beirut at the Lebanese University (a poor cousin of the American establishment), a forcing ground, Chaamaya called it, for Muslim radicals determined to wrest, from their own upper class as well as from Christians, a bigger say in the affairs of the country. They were not necessarily Nasser's men; their road to Socialism was Lebanese. It was interesting that Dr. Zoghal gave lectures to their Law Faculty.

I asked as soon as I could of this student how he considered Dr. Zoghal. Was he a possible leader for them?

He shone darkly. "What he tells us certainly has to come

about! The present Lebanese ruling class cannot hope to prolong forever the farce through which this country is governed. For the world, our liberal Constitution, our free elections, our Chamber of Deputies. In reality—do you know the reality?"

"I haven't caught onto it yet."

He smiled to himself, then began slowly in the manner of the eastern storyteller: "I think I must tell you. It will give you a picture explaining much in our recent history. For, when the French Mandate was ended in 1943, two Lebanese came together, Bishara al-Khuri, the President, a Maronite, and Riad al-Sulh, the Prime Minister, a Muslim. As you are aware, those two posts are the perquisites of those two communities; and similarly down the line to the janitors, with some jobs for the Shia and the Druzes, and the Orthodox Christians, and a Protestant or two. Well, as I was saying, these two gentlemen, aware that they must not allow the French any excuse for coming back and aware of the spoils that go with office, a great benefice following Independence—these two gentlemen, they made a pact together to end the Christian-Muslim feud—at least behind the scenes, where it really mattered—so as not to destroy this benefice, this Lebanon, falling into their laps. There was to be no more wild talk of massacres! No more scheming with European chancelleries. The Christians would surrender their French connection, and the Muslims their more natural Syrian connection. The frontiers, whether just or not, were accepted, and the new national Lebanese flag. . . .

"In fact"—he got excited—"Riad al-Sulh made a tour of each leading Muslim family, and from under his jacket he produced the new flag. This, he told them, is our flag now. We are Arabs together, all Lebanese!"

"Yes, yes," his uncle was smiling, "God be praised! All Arabs at last together."

"But not all of the Faith, uncle!"

The old man smiled as though that too would eventually come to pass. And his nephew continued: "Did the Christians keep their word? I think that the Muslims would have fought them sooner but for those same spoils of office, of which our richer families took a share. It is extraordinary how, among us Muslims, so long as our leaders are publicly benefiting, we accept that the whole community is prospering and being given due recognition. The Christians played a wily game with our leaders, for all their people were grabbing advantages while the mass of Muslims, in the countryside especially, were left without education or amenities. . . .

"And so, of course, came 1958." He paused again, his tone turning sour, but his reconstruction befitting one who aimed to become a lawyer-politician—not, he was to make it plain to me later, of the compromising bourgeois kind, but of the coming Arab Socialist variety. He resumed once more: "Yes, as I say, it would have happened sooner but for the spoils our notables derived from that verbal agreement, that National Pact, *Al-mithaq al-watani*, never written down but the operative basis of our social and political life. Happily, President Chamoun was too greedy! In 1952 he had supplanted Al-Khuri just in time to avert wider trouble. But then he pursued a similar path. Maronite bankers ransacked the economy! Maronites held the best government jobs, far above the agreed proportion. Chamoun was changing the electoral boundaries and trying to force his own reelection beyond the spirit of the Constitution. Also, as known perhaps to you, he was opposing Nasser. It was the aftermath of Suez and in the days of the Egyptian union with Syria, and he was threatening to call in the Americans. Well, that he did, finally, though too late to save himself.

"Muslims like to say"—he paused with a smile for his dear old uncle who had gone over to the window and was sitting apart there, studying a book—"Muslims like to say that they took up arms here in order to reverse Chamoun's foreign policy. They cite the neglect of the Muslim masses. They were ready, they claim, in the name of Arab unity and in the name of Islam's ideal of justice, to link up with Nasser. Lebanon for them, as then known, had proved a failure."

He paused satirically: "Were they being honest? Or was it still a question of the spoils no longer adequately shared with our leaders and with our new leaders who were clamoring to the scene? Let us look at what happened! There was a civil war—but one fought in a most gentlemanly fashion—between bargainers, let us call them, who dare not hurt too much. There were ugly incidents, but Arabs absorb that. In the end General Fuad Shihab, the Maronite Commander-in-Chief who became President, proclaimed the solution of 'fifty-fifty,' *munasafa*, as we say in Arabic. That meant that neither side won, that both sides were to gain equally; equally, that meant first of all between their leaders. True, as a whole, the Maronites disliked it, and true, Shihab's regime began the big shift to bureaucratic power, which would channel revenue to social services and out of the immediate grasp of the chieftains, which is why you will hear Shihab abused, but in essence the *Al-mithaq al-watani* was restored, the unwritten agreement between those who governed."

"Dr. Zoghal is a great Shihabist."

"Yes, yes, I know. There were these reforms, elementary ones to a Western democrat. Any modern State has to take a hand in its country's overall investment requirements. It has to offer services directly. Much was done—with roads, electricity, with education, and civil service reform. Yet today there are still seven hundred villages without a single school, say, a hundred thousand children not in school. Shihab has gone; today's President is weaker. The old chieftain fraternity is back in power—indeed, if it ever lost that power. We hear its confessional parrot cries, which cement the profitable status quo! We watch the impotent farce of the parliament, the scandal of interests leaked to the press, knowing, as we do, that all the real issues have been settled in the St. Georges Hotel bar."

"It is as bad, then, today as in 1958?"

"Perhaps it is worse. Though completely different. Our Muslim leaders, for all their proclamations, have become more tenderfoot. They realize, as much as the Christians do, that their wealth is tied to the independence of Lebanon. In a sense, very good, but it means that they shirk any reform that could really hurt. The Maronites are quick to cry 'Danger!' at the first sign of a serious reform. We shall become the textbook case of immobilism, of platitudinous postponement. To the Socialist it is a cosy nest to explode! We must blow up the Muslims along with the Christians."

"Through one of the parliamentary parties?"

He laughed. "What do these parties amount to? These are chieftain coalitions, assortments of shock troops, a one-man band like the Druze Jumblat. There is the Communist Party, but that is proscribed. We shall form a Socialist Party eventually. Meanwhile, we have to agitate, among students, in the factories a little, like that. . . ."

"So aren't you inevitably driven back to calling on Nasser for outside support? To redress the built-in Christian advantage?"

"No. Not at all. As I have just shown you, that plays into the hands of the Christians. Our older Muslim leaders still do it, or pretend to do it, as a bargaining counter. But we, you understand, we despise them too! They embarrass us, as does Nasser. Leave them to play that little game of blackmail. We shall struggle within the confines of Lebanon."

"Which promises you a rather slow outcome?"

"Let us pray not. There is a wealth of talent within the

submerged Muslim masses. Can our society really spurn that? Just look at how the Maronites have advanced, thanks to foreign help in education. Education remains the key. We shall break through. My generation of students are going to accomplish this. Afterwards, we will know how we did it."

"Is Dr. Zoghal one to help you?"

"Yes. For a time. Then we shall supplant him." He smiled for the first time ingenuously: "He is not finally of our generation."

"And Dr. Hadiri? Is he known to you?"

"Oh yes. In this country all is known. We know very well what he would like to accomplish, especially in this domain of education, but will he—against the big interests? Have you had the honor of meeting his father?"

"Sheik Nassib? Not yet. I hope to. But surely if a powerful Maronite official cannot change the system much, what chance have you?"

"Oh we, we are younger! We are sure to break through!"

And with a smile and politeness worthy of his uncle, he motioned me toward the table where during this time food had been set. The old man joined us. We ate lamb and rice, salad, and yogurt, then very sticky sweetmeats. The radical had a wolfish appetite. With his uncle listening, he discussed Tripoli and the Fair planned for 1970. For a Muslim it was the best city in Lebanon. He was never really at ease in Beirut.

"Thank you. Thank you," I said to the uncle.

"Please do not thank me. You will repay me," he intoned.

"I will walk with you down the suq," said the nephew, as if to protect me from anti-western elements. "You are not afraid to walk everywhere alone?"

"Should I be? If that were so, how could you plan an International Fair here?"

He smiled, touched my arm. "You are right. Forgive me.

Please come again to our house. My uncle asked me particularly to say this. You know, as a young man, at my age, he was very active against the French. That was essential for his generation."

"And now your target has become the Americans?"

"No, no, I was telling you, all these bigger issues disguise the local job to be done. My generation, and that is why we'll succeed, will not be diverted from the local problem."

"Good luck then."

For it might be he, rather an inquiring neutral observer, who one day would fear to walk everywhere alone. This was a country of the razor slash. Could such an honest intelligence survive?

I had intended returning at once to Beirut. I was impatient to get to know the Hadiris. The previous evening I had met Robert Hadiri in the St. Georges bar, and with him a cousin, Raoul Hadiri, who though most misanthropic, reviling the Beirut scene about us, and in particular vexed, it had seemed, by my presence and my maddening desire to have a conversation, was nonetheless fascinating company. Religion aside—and my Muslim encounters had also been pushing me to take an interest in the local political and social scene—I immediately found the Maronites interesting. They were so completely like West Europeans (in a way that even Chaamaya was not), yet here they were, Arabs, in Asia.

Also, this cousin Raoul, representing the one-time Egyptian branch of the family, had a sister, he revealed, called Leila Shemegh. Her husband Youssef had been a Cairene doctor. I was suddenly certain that I had met him. Shemegh? Shemegh? Hadn't there been Shemeghs at the Sporting Club in wartime Alexandria? Cousins again perhaps. I remembered them well.

The misanthrope had softened somewhat. "My sister would welcome other memories of Egypt. She has not got over it. Nor I perhaps. I hope that you will call on us." He had given me his card.

"Our family seer." Dr. Robert had been at pains, once his cousin had left the bar, to efface any disequilibrium. "He can make one feel a bit pedestrian. I recommend you to read his verse." He had proceeded with his own conversation, detached, exploratory, excessively well-mannered. He had professsed entire agreement with Zoghal, but in general terms, avoiding questions. Look, he had seemed to say, at the scene here. Enjoy your drink. I am getting to know you. I am, after all, a civil servant.

He had only opened up when talking of London, and of Paris. Paris he worshipped.

"Come to my office. After ten in the morning you will always find me there. Just ask."

"I will phone you first."

"Oh come. Drop in. It will be a pleasure to talk. At any time."

But that was simply the oriental manner. His westernized mind would dislike it in practice.

We had parted, the mood at least set for discussion. I was keen to be seeing these people again.

Yet at that midday moment in Tripoli, recrossing the Place du Tell to where the Beirut taxis started, I heard the rival cry "Bisharri!"—Bisharri at the head of the Qadisha gorge, a mere thousand feet beneath the Cedars. As I recalled it, it was a village nesting above the sheer wall of the ravine, defying the vertiginous pull downward, with terraced vines and the crash of water and church bells echoing across the void as first one then another sister village joined in a call to matins or vespers, with an approach climbing past dizzy ledges and rock face and heights of scree like so many giants barring the way: the most fabulous single journey in Lebanon. And I turned aside and went to Bisharri. The car already held four passengers, and the roof and boot heaped with sacks. There was time to go and come back, and still go, as I had no things with me, to Beirut before night. The climb was about four thousand feet in thirty-five miles—a sprint for these taxis. Quicker to his seat than I, the driver, as I pulled the door shut, was skidding through the gears. We departed like a rocket through the slummy outskirts, scattering everything Muslim in our path.

This was, of course, a Christian taxi.

The Qadisha gorge (sacred gorge, in Syriac, the form of Aramaic used by the Apostles, and preserved in the liturgy of the Syrian church, of which Nestorians, Gregorians, Copts, Jacobites, Syrian uniates, and Maronites were the contentious near-eastern offshoots) was the original refuge of the Maronites in Lebanon—in this western part of Syria, one should say, for Lebanon as a country is a recent creation. We were heading for the sacred hideout of the sect, sacred because the bluffs of the gorge, down a rock face of six hundred feet, were domesticated with hermits' cells, chapels, monasteries where the rites of the community, and their records, had been faithfully maintained. It was here they had trekked in the seventh century when persecuted by rival churchmen, by Byzantine State and Muslim caliph, and they had joined up with guerrilla bands already harassing the Arab from here. Their patron saint, Maron, had been a monk; they had come to his teaching in the district of Antioch (hence the continuing title of their Patriarch, "Patriarch of Antioch and All the East"—a title disputed by five rival churches); they had founded monasteries along the Orontes; but finally they had trekked to the safety of the mountains.

Since then there had been some hard centuries, and others more bountiful. But here they still were, and nowadays knowing that their children had voyaged and prospered across the world ("this nation!", as successive travelers had called them), and, more important, that, spreading south down the range from high valley to high valley, and so to the foothills, and so to the coast, they had achieved a grip on the land called Lebanon, and through their stubborn Christian allegiance had determined its political independence. They were not its sole inhabitants (though at times they might like to think it); but theirs had been the loudest voice demanding that it should exist separately. They could not suffer the rule of Damascus any more than that of Constantinople. They were, they affirmed, "the true Lebanese"—as Zoghal's sister-in-law had quoted, her elegant face almost spitting with fury, as she had commented, "Those Maronite upstarts!" In any case, they were tough hill folk.

This gorge was their cradle in Lebanon.

I remembered, from the wartime visit to Bisharri, an old man who over his glass of *araq* had recited the Lord's Prayer to us in Syriac. Their liturgy, of course, was still in that tongue. An old Semitic noise. There was a priest, it seemed, still teaching it weekly to the local children. A strange old noise. The tongue of Jesus Christ? It had disturbed us as something infinitely alien from the pressing concerns of contemporary life.

I asked the driver now, in French, "Do you yourself speak any Syriac? You know, Aramaic? As in the Liturgy?"

He laughed. He appeared to think I was a crank. They were gabbling in Arabic. We were pounding uphill through the olive groves at the north tip of the Kura, the almost wholly Greek Orthodox plain, itself already a thousand feet up, that spreads like a delta at the mouth of the gorge. Here, less protected, the Orthodox Christians had compromised more with the Muslims, with the powerful emirs governing from Tripoli—a geography and a history that affected them still. Theirs was a lesser voice in Lebanon—today, if one had to judge from the press, disposed mainly to peck at the Maronites.

"No, I do not." He had discussed it with the company before actually giving his answer. They were a square-faced, tanned, rugged group of men, intent on some problem, and they were scanning the road and the olive groves with some anxiety. But they turned to me now as though my peculiar question forced them to see just who I was, a stranger obviously, but a liability? They conveyed unlimited ruthlessness.

"Say, friend, but I think you must be British!" A wizened smile was enveloping the face of the passenger over to the far left. "You fooled me for a moment, but I can see you are British! Well, I am Australian! And my brother here!"—hands were extending—"You fooled us for a moment. We're glad to meet you. We're glad to see you with us. These two fellows at the front are planning to return with us to Australia later, but they don't as yet speak much English. I don't think the driver speaks English." The driver and I also shook hands, his gaze and arm leaving the chauffeuring to the guidance of God for several seconds. We garbled something in French to each other.

But it was predominantly a Commonwealth moment.

"Excuse me while I speak my language," said the first one, and he rattled off some sentences in Arabic with a harshness and an expressiveness totally lacking in his lazy Australian, adding to the complexity of one's view of an Arab. Then he settled, for most of the journey, for English. As he confessed, "I am not happy in this country. Oh, they cheat you! John,"—very soon we had moved to a Christian name exchange: Jim, Peter, Wally, Maroun—"how they cheat you! They just think about money. All the time they are thinking how to get your money. I can't stay any more in this country."

All four passengers came from Qannubin, the community beneath the Bisharri road, vertically down at the base of the ravine where also stood their oldest monastery, virtually a fortress through the early centuries, built within a vast natural cavern ten minutes up the cliffside. Almost inaccessible. "We'll take you there, John. We don't mind that path down the cliff. You have to see the treasures. You'll want to tell your people that you have been to holy Qannubin in Lebanon. There's a road being built by the Electric Company, but we don't need to go by that."

They themselves were staying in Bisharri, where they were developing summer apartments. They had repatriated their capital to Lebanon to invest it in the holiday trade. The rents, they explained, were for their families still toiling away in the valley.

"They should not live like that nowadays. We'd take them with us, but it's nice to keep a link. We're going to make it good for them here. Lebanon's the most beautiful country in the world, John. It's only—it's a hard life, so they cheat you. You know, they shoot if they get offended. My mind could not rest here now."

No sooner had Jim uttered this opinion than Wally told me to sit well down. We were approaching Zgharta, and between this village and the men of Bisharri there was some ugly feeling. A posse of soldiers stood at the entrance with an armored car. There had been shooting affrays; one never quite knew when the next shot might be fired. There were motorcycle police stationed up the street, who as soon as they saw us signaled us on: quick, quick, pass through the village. "We aren't going to loiter," snorted Jim. To the casual eye life looked normal, even rather sleepy in doorway and alley; and it was now mentioned that our driver passed up and down this route each day. Still, one never knew. "It adds excitement. But John, I just couldn't live in this country. Australia, that's the place for my children."

As we climbed above the village, they kept glancing back and never relaxed their watch on the roadside, not till we had climbed as high as Ihden and the wavy plain was far beneath us, ebbing out to its puny cliffs and the sun-flashing sea beyond. More strikingly below us now was the gorge thrusting and twisting into the mountains. Every slope, every drop was exaggerated; stretched to give this vertical effect. How could sheep cling to that angle, how could soil and trees remain? It was five miles or so across to where the other enclosing ridge unfolded, and behind it the cedar woods of Hadath, with a road corresponding to ours descending, cork-screwing away to the plain, and nearer, between us, the momentous gulf, darkening as it twisted and narrowed into the innermost slit of the ravine.

"We are going to show you Yusuf Karam's body."

We had got round to talking of Maronites. They attended their Maronite church in Brisbane, which, together with Lebanese food and newspapers, was as much a part of their antipodal life as sharks and aborigines. I had asked them what they recalled of their history, and this, though it brought pride to their faces, also brought some hesitation.

"We have always been in these mountains, John—before the Arabs, we fought the Arabs—we helped the Crusaders to take Jerusalem. I think the Arabs have never forgiven us for keeping our minds open to the West. You see, that's it; our priests went to Rome—after we had become joined to Rome—and they brought back new western ideas. We threw off the Arab feudal system. You understand, we could not stay down. . . ."

"They lambasted us after the Crusades, after the Crusaders had gone back home!" Wally remembered more somber events. "They came for taxes; the Turks followed them. I would agree that they resented our freedom; but this high valley and its saints protected us. We escaped the 1860 troubles when the Druzes butchered our people to the south.

The Druzes butchered thousands of Christians through the low hills of Matn and Shuf, and in the Biqa'; and the Turks assisted. In a single day, over in Damascus, they put to death five thousand Christians! The events of '60." He shook his head. "It is all written down. You think we forget? Though it never halted the Maronite advance. I agree with Jim: the priests sustained us, and they spearheaded each advance. Priests and monks. And then there was the silk trade. . . ."

"And Yusuf Karam!" Maroun, still struggling with the beginnings of English, stopped short with this name.

"Yes, say wait! There's an idea! We'll take John in to see Karam's body. It's a miracle, John. You have to see it."

So on entering Ihden, we stopped by the church that stood above the view like a fortress. There was a ruined Byzantine chapel near, and restful arbors of pine and cypress, and a veritable eden of jonquil and crocus. But the party, after commending the air and sending a boy to fetch them water, turned to the statue of Yusuf Bey, mounted on horse with drawn saber, the mettlesome man who had defied the Turks during the latter nineteenth century.

In fact, Yusuf Bey had personified conservative elements among the Maronites at that particular epoch, furious, with the ending of the Druze feudal order and the signing of the international statute that wound up the events of '60 and so set limits to Turkish power, that they were not to govern the Mountain. He, and not someone from Constantinople, Karam had felt, should be the governor. With French encouragement he had seen himself as the hero of a drive for Christian independence. The Turks obstinately had blocked his path. He had rebelled once or twice. He had been exiled to France, and he had died in Naples in 1889.

Who then was this figure before us? For by now we had trooped into the church, led by an old woman with keys to the tomb, she told us in a sunken whisper, of that saint,

God praise him, Yusuf Karam. There within a glass case he lay, his skin a wizened ivory texture, as if it were now part of the bone. "He was never embalmed. A miracle, John." One looked down at the shrunken figure, eerie within its glass container, with the high-naved church quavering above us and the sunlight visibly edging away, and really it was a moment for ghostly laughter. But Jim continued in sober Australian, "He has not decomposed. We are seeing a miracle." The others perfunctorily agreed and gave money.

They took water from the font and crossed themselves.

"We had to show you the miracle, John. I hope you don't mind." Back in the taxi, pounding along the road again, a certain fresh air good sense was returning. "If you stay some time, we can show you the Cedars. We are going to have a good time here."

There were only another seven miles to cover, but these skirted the lip of the ravine, with villages over on the other side within hailing distance. Immediately below were the crags, then drops—an Alpinist's practicing ground—down to the fertile, watery floor, a meadow of trees and crops to gaze on for all those cliff-inhabiting monks, and a well of soft, watery music for those like ourselves who stopped for a moment and peered uncertainly over the brink.

Above, before us—an alternative view in which I was engaging Jim's attention: for that was Qannubin down below, and laconically he was proposing the descent—were the two highest peaks of the range, Kornet es Sauda and Jebel Mneitri, and between them the col, and the bowl beneath it, still ablaze with winter snow, where the last four hundred of the most famous cedars were grouped in a dark, protected patch. Solomon's cedars, cedars used for temples to Baal along the coast. An unnerving country, which mile by mile caught one in a different page of history.

"Yes," rumbled Wally, whose lugubrious mind seemed

slowly to rechew its thoughts, "even over in Brisbane some-times we talk about the events of '60."

"We show you—Yusuf Karam himself," parroted the lad Maroun.

Jim, however, had moved to the present. "How about our going skiing tomorrow? There is still good, crisp snow up there. We can be photographed beside the Cedars. The Cedars of God, John, did you know that? They are very holy trees for Maronites. Friend, we shall have a good time here."

He was the arranger, the older brother. He arranged the evening *araq* party. Relatives by the drove appeared, some in unpressed city suits—they also were travelers from Bris-bane—and others came in grubby mountain wear, and one in the old-style *sharwal* and boots with a corded *kuffieh* headdress. They all shared the mountain look, and a liking for *araq*, and the same talk, in this mixed-up Australian-Arabic, of making money and their future overseas. They did not care about Beirut and the modern Constitution of Lebanon. They saw themselves as beyond all that, as the Lebanese of coming generations who, one by one, if they knew what was good for them, would become transformed into Australians or Americans. "Why stay here in this small country? You are always somebody else's poor. Do I want to look to Tripoli as the outlet for my day's labor? You are hemmed in here. There is no space."

Another told a story: "They used to say that the world was Asia and that Asia was Turkey, and that the best of Turkey at that time was Lebanon, and that in Lebanon first and last came Bisharri, and that up in Bisharri there was an old man, and—whoever was telling it used to add—that old man is me!"

Jim commented, "That just shows you! John, I feel that I've known you a lifetime. Come to Brisbane. Bring your family. My mind won't rest till I'm back in Brisbane. *Ahlan wa sahlan*, as they say in my language."

He went in search of another jug of *araq*. The room was thick with fumes and a growing incoherence in the conversation. Who cared about the Sixth Fleet's visit! Who cared about Abdul Nasser! There were open spaces, wads of currency, and the great English-speaking freedoms waiting for you over there in Australia. All you needed was a one-way ticket.

"But you care about Arabic. You say you read your papers, that you never miss receiving them from Lebanon."

"I just like to know what the bastards are doing!"

It was such a good party, with various women in the background serving up food and hiccupping with laughter and, later in the evening, singing and shouting with an unmistakably ribald stridency, that it seemed that the morrow could only be a letdown. So when someone spoke of going to a night club down in Tripoli, I angled in, and madly, murderously, we completed the descent, swinging from one chasm to the next, with one of the fellows firing a revolver as if to alert the whole of Zgharta. And in Tripoli itself there was a hair-raising quarrel, undilutedly Arab, and I made myself scarce. And I still found a taxi for Beirut.

Next morning, having a coffee in the sun at my favorite spot down rue Hamra, a London *Times* to exercise thought, the previous evening seemed about as likely as a trip on marijuana.

❧◊❧

An Approach to the Clan

I decided to call on Raoul Hadiri. It was a possible hour. I was by chance in the quarter; the cool sea breeze, blowing around the corner, put me in mind of Alexandria. There was the same kind of hopeless refuse, of cans and paper and scraps of food all drenched in rotting fruit, on the pavement beside the tall modern building. There was a vacant lot with an abandoned car, palms, and the temporary hut of a man selling sandwiches to laborers. Other blocks of apartments were rising. There was one down the street about half completed, a tangle of rods and concrete with nine-inch brick walls slapped up, which seemed already on the point of collapse. Though otherwise, with a convent school, some faceless wall, tiny shops and a garage, there were still a few traditional dwellings, arabesqued and triple-arched, worked with stucco and marble inlay, rising through three or four balcony levels to large flat roofs for the laundry.

These old buildings either ran together or were only a slit of an alley apart. And behind them was an agglomeration of first floor extensions and of smaller houses built in the old gardens or courtyards, intricately joined by stairways and bridges or by high boundary walls. It was a warren of dilapidation, soon to go, but pleasant still—apart from the smell of the drains that hit you. And it overlooked the sea front near to the big hotels and the cabarets, so it had a sort of timeless air. There was a café, with the slap of backgammon counters, the sound of the *dhobi* man resting his iron, and the drift past of errand boy's feet. It was not so different from Alexandria. And emboldened by memories and by instinct bidding me to call without first arranging the visit, I entered this most modern of the buildings and took the elevator to the top floor.

A maid answered. Monsieur Raoul was out. I was beginning to jot a few words on a card when an agitated voice could be heard inquiring who the visitor was. Englishman, I conveyed to the maid in basic Arabic, and, as an afterthought, Englishman from Egypt. Moments later I was in a comfortable chair, facing Leila Shemegh.

She was gracious, yet beset with anxiety. There were newspapers tumbled to the floor, and she looked as if she had been sitting and brooding and that, on top of that, the arrival of a stranger might foreshadow something worse. Her heavy face and build suggested that she was a prey to terrible palpitations. What, she began, in rounded English, was the latest news from Egypt?

I had to admit that I didn't know, though I hoped to go there during the summer. I mentioned one or two people I should visit. In a second we were both recalling the past, Gezira, the Nile, the beach at Alexandria, and the glamor (never to be deeply examined) of that privileged Levantine society. I think we hit it off. By now she had remembered something that Raoul had mentioned ahead. And possibly she already saw in me yet one more person she could discreetly mother. Arab minds soar, weave fantasies easily. And retrospectively I am sure that Leila, seizing on the fact that I was a traveler, and alone, had already thought up meals and companions and arrangements for further little chats like this so that she could feel she was looking after me.

As the maid brought the coffee, Leila bid her go back for that especially good *halva* in the kitchen.

But she was still suspicious. It was axiomatic that a pleasant prospect hid trouble. Furrows of anxiety returned. "Shemegh?" she queried. "Are you sure that it was Antoine Shemegh you knew in Alexandria?" I could show it, but still she twisted and doubted and produced new queries and put off the moment of feeling perfectly at ease and secure. And she turned to bewailing the fate of Egypt and of all those trusting *fellahin* (that *melaya*-and-*gallabieh* throng slip-slopping forever through memory). And she said that she feared there would be trouble in Lebanon. Trouble followed you through these countries. Just to look at the papers made her nervous.

"But why do you read them, then, Madame?"

On the floor beside her, beside her spectacles, were copies of *L'Orient* and *Al Nahar*, the leading local right-wing papers, and, to offset these, the Egyptian-inspired, rabble-rousing *Al Muharrer* and the Cairo weekly, *Rose al-Youssef*. Excellent, doubtless, in some of their features, they all competed in brinkmanship when it came to reporting Middle East affairs. They were like the several flames of a fire, raging this way and that with the wind, giving off the most lurid light. It was wiser, for the world's press was available, to steady down with *The Times* or *Le Monde*.

"Why do you read them, Madame?" I repeated, for she was brooding, shaking, I almost thought for a moment, with a kind of inexpressible panic.

"One cannot afford to be caught again." She fell silent. She essayed, "How can I explain!" She was sighing. "I was so happy in Egypt. And Raoul. We considered ourselves Egyptians. My father did so much for that country. He worked, like many Lebanese who went there, to bring about a cultural improvement. It became cosmopolitan. It grew in scale. You know, they say that we have brought it here now—you see it in the shops, in business thinking—now that we have been forced to return. But why did it happen? Tell me please. *Bidnā na'ish*—we want to live! Why are there people in the world against that? I am afraid that it can also happen here."

As I tried to console her, she was suddenly laughing, weakly, her big bosom heaving: "I can tell you, my dear, I have a bad dream sometimes. I find myself in a railway station with my luggage lost and the train just leaving. I don't know what to do! Then I ask myself: is it a dream or something from the future? You laugh, my dear"—it was she who was laughing—"but it is not easy to live in these countries." Soft tears were appearing. She was not embarrassed. She was still perhaps picturing herself impoverished and abandoned, and philosophically embracing it.

Yet she looked well protected here.

"Where is Raoul? Where can my brother have got to?" She glanced sharply round. Then her gaze became lost in the wider view floating through the window—the pellucid sea on that April afternoon, the racing craft hoisting their sails, and beyond, beyond her plants and the rooftops and the squealing pigeons and some low, still cloud, the ever-miraculous soaring mountains dark green and grey, with only specks of snow. The summer was at last arriving.

"It is very beautiful, isn't it," she said, "Lebanon? *Inshâ'llâh*, I shall end my days here."

She fell, without pause, into languorous reverie, utterly passive and without complaint, a favorite afternoon mood, one could guess, in this sun-baked, very comfortable apartment. Panic was for odd moments only.

"I can't think where Raoul can be," she intoned to herself. "Hoda!" Her voice rang out. The maid appeared. She stared at the girl, a very sweet little creature, unaffected and calm. She spoke to her in Arabic, almost dreaming again, then dismissed her, then called her back: "Oh Hoda! More coffee. And bring the liqueurs." She explained, "I am giving her French instruction. She wishes to be like people in the city. Her brute of a fiancé would like to marry her and carry her back to their mountain village." She sighed. "I have responsibilities."

Over a liqueur and chocolate cake she asked me, "At which hotel are you staying?" I told her. At first she pretended not to know it. "Isn't it a little uncomfortable there?"

With barely a pause: "How much could you afford—to pay, that is, for a comfortable room? Or an apartment?"

She brushed past my hesitation—for Arabs like to spell money out—and explained, "One hears of rooms occasionally.

Raoul might know of an apartment. I will think of it, my dear. You ought to be comfortable." She smiled lazily. We had become friends.

As she now had another visitor ringing, I took my leave without meeting Raoul, but then I unexpectedly met him that evening. There was a charity ball in aid of village children (villages where it took half a year's work for a man to raise the price of a donkey, eight days' work for the price of a hen), and, of course, it was a lavish affair. Not one hen but dozens had been slaughtered, and turkeys, calves, suckling pigs, salmon. There was a long buffet table and it groaned with salvers and dishes of rice and bowls of salad and all kinds of egg savories and caviar and other tidbits. And these good things were repeated at intervals so that swarms of guests could start feeding together. Beyond the heavy meats and the fish were the cheese platters with an assortment of breads, and beyond these a selection of sweets (so that you were all like huge ships tying up at the wharf next to your loading bays), and here there were waiters who spurned your efforts merely to take a large portion of tart or bombe glacé or strawberries or mousse and who seized your plate and seemed to spoon onto it the entire contents of the dish you had chosen, ready, it seemed, if you thought to demur, to pour the excess down your shirt front. Jack, like his master, was reveling in abundance. Vast replenishments were continuously arriving, and the only course was to eat away and to marvel that girls slender as dewdrops could all the time eat so much more.

Outside the hotel, in the noisy night, chauffeur-strongmen guarded the cars. In the foyer the expensive tickets were collected, and a first array of girls were stationed selling nice flowers and perfumes and so on, very pretty girls of rather rich families, and all along, through the hall for dancing, and down throughways and beside the bars, as if by some haunting mirror effect these girls were endlessly repeated, selling perfumes, cigarettes, flowers, programs, cigarettes, perfumes—girls no different from other guests except, as they were openly selling something, their brilliantly dark eyes and hair flashed with a special satisfaction. It suited the mores of a merchant community. They had a head start on the mood of the night.

The hall was filling, close to the stage, for dancing now and a show later. At tables set with champagne or whiskey convoys of young people were arriving, confirming their table, then drifting to the floor or for drinks at the bar or down to the buffet.

At surrounding tables, and at some on the balcony giving a dress circle view, somewhat older women were gathering (if one can employ the word "old" where eternal youth was so ardently fought for), heavy with jewels and eye shadow, their pulpy flesh displayed as fully as that of their freshly petalled daughters. In them, perhaps, could better be seen the amazing mixture of peoples here, from dusky Assyrian to fair Circassian, from hairy, fine-boned Armenian to spade-faced Turk. Long head, round head, Persian, Kurd, mixture of the aquiline nose of the desert and the fleshy lips with a hill squatness. Over all perhaps an oily veneer through love of skin preparations and through common indulgence in an oily diet.

These rich ships, in part chaperone, in part odalisque still in the swim, had gathered for a watchful eye on the scene, to prise open secrets and to gloat; and some stayed anchored there all evening, as if movement were foreign to their nature, and a pall of boredom settled on them; but mostly they drifted down to the buffet to eat, to catch up with their husbands capering along with friskier vessels, and to signal in an infinite variety of ways the young men they personally favored.

These signals were so fast and frequent, in a society where

everybody was known down to the last rumor and conceit, down to the latest trading triumph that no tax man would ever hear of, that they rivaled in finesse the activity of a bourse. One appetite helped the other in that quicksilver throng pushing to the buffet.

I had left the Americans who had brought me here, and I was trying to catch Dr. Zoghal. His Byronic figure moved at speed. Because every face one passed was interesting—that mercantile arrogance, that Phoenician cynicism, those silver sequins setting off a chignon that set off the most honeyed sweetness—I kept losing ground. But then, there he was, for an instant holding the hand of a girl, tall, concentratedly thoughtful, not among the youngest but overlaying this aspect with her long hair pouring down a kaftan and her full mouth open with eagerness. Then he had gone, and she was smiling to herself. But in the next instant she was talking nimbly, with rather forceful speech, one noticed as one drew near to her, to another man who had halted there. He was bearing plates of food, so he soon passed on; then she too was lost in the crowd.

Turning, I saw Raoul. He appeared to have been watching the same small episode as I, and he beckoned me over, his gimlet gaze sweeping all the room in our vicinity, so that the moment I joined him he said in general terms, "One has to be rather young to enjoy this. Or a rugger blue." He emphasized "blue" as a word in that sense outside his usage but one he was happy to proffer to me.

I realized that he was feeling friendly, that whatever mood, or test, he had felt obliged to impose during our previous encounter was no longer required. I felt much relieved.

I blessed his sister. Though, aside from that, he was a practitioner in moods.

He had swung away from where Zoghal had been, and he was conducting me in the opposite direction. "I must introduce you to Robert's father, who is, as you will have gathered, the head of our clan." He emphasized "clan" as though to indicate that it had perhaps archaic links, then embroidered, "Don't be misled by appearance. We are tribesmen still, and one man holds almost the power of life and death within his own tribal domain. He, also, is governed by rules. But a powerful chieftain is firstly an illusionist. Here you are meeting a powerful chieftain."

The gentleman in question, in deep conversation, affable and fluent, with two other men, like all males present, in dinner jackets, had the air of a successful company director who had once battled up from the floor. He had been long at the top, but he had not lost the ruggedness attending his beginnings. In some way he registered our approach and, without actually slowing his speech, put out an arm to Raoul with a sort of shaggy animal movement that was both a guard and an extension of protection; then he was facing us and smiling as if we were deadly slow in stating our business. "My dear Raoul, I am surprised to see you. You must be surprised to see me too. I never go to parties. It is enough that Maurice and Les Jeunes Filles, as you call them, are here."

Raoul grinned. "Sheik, it is said that in one year you managed to attend every birth and engagement celebration in the entire district that you represent! Apocryphal, surely, with those mountain winters."

"Good for breeding in, eh?" It was an earthy laugh. "Alas, times are changing. It is an argument, cousin, for also doing all that we can to raise the living standards of the Muslims. Then perhaps they will breed less too."

He was already halting another guest and saluting, beginning to turn away from us, when Raoul very quickly introduced me as a writer, as a friend—I was surprised to hear him say—of the Sheik's son Robert, and of Dr. Hamid Zoghal. I had, after all, only met Robert once. But Raoul's voice was smooth with implications. After a month in Lebanon I knew that no possibility is left unexploited. By simply being there, one was used in some way, by different people, for their current concerns. I was quite content to see where this took me.

The Sheik's arm had now gripped me with a slightly feline tenacity as though connecting the blood streams, like a doctor sounding something out. Although he was exchanging a rapid word, his face turned away with the new arrival. He had not actually looked at me yet but had seemed to absorb my presence via Raoul. Then abruptly his bland, unblinking features—not particularly friendly features, with the pressure of myriad interests within them—were confronting me as if to conjecture what it was that I wanted. No doubt he was deciding what he might want, but he was able to convey the opposite.

His arm stayed connected. He was suggesting a talk. I should come to his office one day next week. Raoul was to fix it with his secretary.

Then his bushy eyes were blazing, with a feeling that one could see he was using to supersede whatever he had just decided about me, as he declaimed, "I have always said that the British moved out of this area too soon. There were other ways of playing it. Your Eden was right." He noted that my face showed disagreement. He smiled. In a quite different voice he continued, "Dear sir, I look forward to our talk next week."

As we moved off, Raoul's smile contorted as if it were a kitten playing with wool. "You have made an impression," he said flatteringly. We were heading for the buffet. "Can you stand this crush? Is there anybody else that you want to meet?" He looked around with distaste, though to several individuals he signaled a message of consolation. "That *poule de luxe,* for instance, over there? Married twice, with a bizarre collection of false antiques from her first husband. Bored, like most of these women are bored. Beirut is an immense brothel. As a writer—"

He was cut off by the clasp of an old gentleman who looked extremely touched to see him. For a moment Raoul too looked natural, chattering happily. Then the moment was over.

"A fellow poet. He is reading this evening. He will start off the amateur cabaret. That's true of us, too: we like games, charades, simple home and family pleasures. You must disentangle it for yourself. By the way, monsieur"—we still called each monsieur—"my sister thinks that you might be interested in a vacant apartment that we have downstairs. On the third floor, at the back, tiny; the permanent tenant is in Europe this summer. It is left with us to sublet or not."

A surge of gratitude settled it for me. Never mind the rent. (Which they later fixed, with the exact levantine perspicacity, without having to ask me, at the figure I could afford.)

"Think it over," he was saying, distancing himself. He was now deciding he would not eat anything. A wave of the hand and he had gone, leaving, like the Cheshire Cat, a sardonic smile.

I rejoined the Americans and stayed for the cabaret. As he said, it was a type of college review put on for friends and relations. The laughs were laughs for cousin Georges or for Papa making a fool of himself. The crowd that till now had packed the buffet came to cheer and, more than ever, recorded their own excessively mercurial energy. One could not imagine a room of people flashing with more push or shrewdness. It might not go so much further than that, toward wit or creative achievement; but the other gloss they had, and youth, and resilience, brokers' qualities, qualities that were useful

for the quick trick or the passing affair, and with more
sedate years for the amassing of fortunes. They sat or stood
in family groups; tough fighting units each one.

Clearly, they all knew one another, within this inner tent
of their society. Money was the great mixer here. Here was
the association of interest, condemned by the young rebel
in Tripoli that, waiving principle, managed the country. I
had the feeling that if I wanted to see something of the inner
workings of Lebanon—which by now I did—here were the
people best placed to show it to me. Raoul's suggestion was
a way in. He had only mentioned it after he had seen that
I would be acceptable to the Sheik, the arbiter in all tribal
details. I might have to move under their wing, a limiting
view in some respects and liable to cut me off from others.
But worth it. A kind of open sesame within their immediate
circle. Arabs, once a certain barrier was crossed, never did
the rest by halves.

An odd tug of feeling. It is comfortable to stay like a
tourist on the outside. To go in with people is full of hazard.
Bruises, disenchantment: these may also follow.

The earliest morning sounds in the quarter were the hurried
talk and the footsteps of cabaret artists returning to their
beds. Some of the doors in the surrounding warren, close
to an espresso bar and cake shop, led to their particular
pensions. A cat meowed. The gulls came over. Distant traffic
sounds increased. In our building a baby somewhere began
urgently to cry Mamma. The military woman on the ground
floor threw open her shutters with a clang to let in the air
to her canaries.

Two hours later the whole place was astir. The little shops
were open for business. The maids sent down for bread and
papers, remembered to leave shoes with the cobbler, who

worked in a crib of a semi-basement with his head showing at pavement level. The electrician was open. The *dhobi* man was open, though only his assistant moped about as yet, dropping ash among the washing. An uncle of the grocer took a chair to the pavement to read his paper in the crisp morning air. A boy from the café brought him a coffee, *masbout*, of medium sweetness, and he sat there, reading his paper and flicking his beads and scowling at other versions of the news humming off the transistor radios.

Our concierge appeared about now. He had stomach trouble; he coughed in the mornings. The military woman was a great complainer and she tackled him the moment he appeared. In her dressing gown she strode to the barrow of an itinerant fruit and vegetable man and vociferously argued the price of the goods. She did not have a maid, she had lived in the building that had preceded these new apartments, and she had obtained a special rent from Leila. She posed as a moral force in the neighborhood, and her mixture of screechy French and Arabic reached a higher pitch through the morning as the gossip moved from balcony to balcony. The concierge foolishly fed her with gossip, thinking perhaps in this way to placate her. Only concerning the Hadiri family, and the comings and goings of Les Jeunes Filles, did she seemingly never say a word. In any case, in the afternoons she slept.

About mid-morning Leila's maid, Hoda, came down to do my apartment. There were two rooms, with kitchen and bathroom, decorated in studio style. The usual occupant was a young architect, who had earned quick money in Kuwait and was taking further studies in Rome. He was a collector of prints and of figurines, and these were showed off well by the lighting. There were some rugs, but Leila did not think there were enough, nor enough cushions nor flower jars, and almost each time that Hoda appeared she brought some addition to the furnishing. I considered it best to go out while she worked, and looking back from the street, I could see all those rugs being shaken and beaten and placed over the balcony for air. The house fronts were a picture in the mornings, with goat and camel *kilims*, Turkish prayer rugs, carpets from Shiraz and Samarkand, with an occasional rare Ispahan or old Kirman glowing with roses, or a thick soft Kazak or Circassian: relics of intermarriage and movements (often swift in Ottoman times) from all corners of this populous region that had somehow come to a halt in Beirut, down here, not far from the harbor.

Hoda was a phenomenal worker. She scrubbed the floors with kerosene. She whisked all the dust out of sight and took a broom down the central stairs that were really the concierge's province. In the kitchen I only made coffee and toast and an occasional egg and slice of bacon, but there she polished every copper pan (which, sign of change, the owner was collecting from Leila's crony, Sarkoubian, who in turn got them from peasant households eagerly changing to aluminum), and she carried off my laundry to the *dhobi* and suits for pressing and things to be sewn. A man could not do that for himself. One Friday she arrived shortly before a muezzin could be heard calling to the Faithful. She stood on the balcony crossing herself.

By now the day was going full blast, especially with the roar of arriving planes amplified between the high buildings. For some moments conversation would be drowned. Then again from over the school wall children's voices could be heard competing; a car leaving the garage revved till it reached the pitch of a pig squealing, then braked as sharply, for no apparent reason; the peddlers passed, calling nostalgically; the noise from the building site fell away as the laborers squatted down to their sandwiches. Some of them went to an eating place for salads and yogurt and sometimes kebabs. Soon the white collar workers would be back, taking the elevators to their family lunches. Cooking smells filled the street.

The afternoons gave a different picture. They were slower and, alas, smellier, from the drains and the garbage heaps sweating with flies, and they seemed quieter. One seemed to hear more of the minor sounds from the craftsmen's shops and of the backgammon counters from the café tables and of the laughter of a maid who had slipped out. Many people were taking a siesta. The temperature was up in the seventies. Many people were still arguing the politics they had raised at lunch. It was the clandestine hour for certain couples, and about this time the cabaret performers shook themselves and came out for a coffee. Toward four the traffic increased, and the ritual of visiting friends and relatives and of sending maids for cakes and chocolates and of looking in at one's dressmaker, started. This, one could see, was the hour that Leila, through the day till now, had been waiting for.

If one did not call on her, she wailed, "My dear, why are you deserting me?" She meant it. She would punish one with her distress for some minutes.

So it came about that if I could not call, through some other engagement, I telephoned, and made my apology, and so was forgiven.

I learned that all the Hadiris in Beirut telephoned Leila at least once a week to keep her in a nice equilibrium, and they told their children to ask her blessing. Their chauffeur-driven cars kept arriving in turn, giving the street an extra importance. It was a form of easily dispensed charity, for I gather that they all pitied her slightly. Yet equally she was known to be dear to the Sheik. Her advice, though full of sighs and pauses, was often the most constructive available (it was free of the grudges and the snobberies and cleverness that bedevilled their Beiruti mentalities). And she offered a sweet moment up in that room, with her cakes and plants and panoramic sunshine, more real, I once heard Les Jeunes Filles exclaiming, than anywhere else in that blessed town. Those girls of course had other reasons. Aunty was a blanket alibi. They did in fact turn up most days; in principle, they always did.

Other lesser people, like the Armenian, who did not have a telephone—and who for centuries had known it as most unwise to write anything down on paper, and by extension were suspicious of cables and phones—sent, if they could not go, some relative. This humble person hovered near Leila or waited out in the hall or kitchen, sometimes with a snip of a rug to sell her or some relic from the Holy Land or some Muslim charm (for Leila saw wisdom, and protective power, in Islam also). And then he would be given cakes and coffee, as if he were the Sheik himself. Then Leila, with her favorite *"Tayyib, tayyib"* (literally "very well," but in her case "I may do") or *"Hadir"* ("presently"), stopped thinking about him, stopped noticing his presence, and he faded out.

Sarkoubian himself was never dismissed. If one of the Hadiris arrived, or some fellow widow from Egypt, he retreated somewhere. It was as if, so silent was his departure, he had passed through the wall or turned himself into a tiny beetle on the carpet. He did not retreat to kitchen or hall, and even Raoul would say, "Where is he?" Then, recalled, he was sidling to her chair, removing his tarbush and dabbing his pate, mysteriously manifested again. Raoul concluded: "You Armenians, you are such an ancient people, I suppose that you just fade back into history! What were the Sumerians like, Sarkoubian? How was it, living in Nineveh?" Sarkoubian relished that sort of joke.

Did he in fact even live in their apartment? No, he could be seen leaving, and loitering, chatting to people in other doorways. But he was very much with Leila, her spy and confidant, and the source of much that she later voiced. Raoul did not always care for him.

Other people came, villagers with gifts, villagers and townsmen who favored Leila as the way to reach the Sheik's ear. It was so oriental in that in many of these cases they could quite simply have spoken to the Sheik but preferred an intermediary. Leila, with no ambitions of her own, with such a good heart, was most people's choice. The bell of her apartment was constantly ringing. "A word in your ear!" mimicked Raoul. "My dear sister, you should stuff them with wax!"

Still, he appreciated the jams, the raisins and dried figs, the young vine leaves, the fresh mountain bread and mountain cheese that appeared on their table through these visitors. Hoda's fiancé called each day (for a look at her) with some contribution. Leila during a discussion of medicinal herbs, once showed me her kitchen store—it smelled of cinnamon, onions, parsley. She was saying, "My dear, if you get diarrhea, I've got mint and laban and quince, or sumac. Coriander is good if you feel dizzy. Carob is good for constipation. And pumpkin seeds will cure worms." And before she shut the door, I was counting the jars of pickled vegetables, pastes, oil, lentils, burghul, orange blossom essence. . . .

The ledger balanced. It was a two-way traffic.

I was very hesitant at first in calling on her by simply ringing the bell, but there she was insisting, "Every day at four. You laugh, you think we talk that way, eh? We exaggerate?" She could look most fearsome. "My dear, I am showing you how we feel. The Arab heart is the biggest in the world! You cannot understand how we love humanity. We expect our friends to be with us all the time; there can be no limit. You must eat with us, every day, if you wish to."

All the same, what with Raoul's moods, which could

escalate to a tantrum or lay him flat in bed for a day and were always lurking with some malevolence (as equally with a need for friendship), I kept to a brief teatime visit, unless specifically asked to something else. I made my report to Aunty Leila, embroidering it with an interest in Maronites, hoping that would go round the clan.

It was to prove the perfect entrée.

At the flat I usually met the girls—the teenage cousins thought of as nieces, as they thought of her as Aunty-from-Egypt—and vaguely I recollected two of them from the crush at the charity ball. Yola and Lulu and Marie-Rose, and their friends Mona and Coco and Gaby—delectable girls, each so lively, so bronzed and vivid from skiing and sailing, and so arrogantly pleased with the life spread before them, and yet so vulnerable, that they seemed interchangeable. Yola, a daughter of the Sheik, was toughest, with large, heavily shadowed eyes and fluent fingers, and a challenging way of giving her opinions.

On an early occasion she was discussing Sami, her older brother who "made money out of pleasure"—"*il se fait payer les plaisirs!*" In a way, she admired him; he had come to terms with the hypocritical adult reality. The affair of the maid had been his début. For Gaby's sake she retold that incident. He had debauched a maid—poor girl, only twelve. Then, scared of his father, he had packed her off and actually sold her to a school friend's family. The gain had pleased him. He had gone after the girl, and subsequently he had sold her five times, each time posing as her agent (her parents being peasants in Syria) so he could take the year's payment. Then a few weeks later he had sold her again. He had had to suborn one policeman. The girl had ended in the Burj somewhere.

"He is a wicked man," commented Leila. "I love him, but his father should have thrashed him. Where is the honor in acting like that? Does he act much differently now even though he has become so prominent socially?"

"He deserves a knife in his back," muttered Raoul, who had left his rooms (separate study and bedroom) to join us for tea. Raoul looked as if he had just woken up; though he pretended that he had been working. "I am excessively busy." He added now, "It is difficult to accept that we have an individual like Sami in the family."

But he was in the family; and Sami Hadiri was not an uncommon type in Beirut.

I think the girls saw me as a friend of Raoul's, a bit fuzzy-minded when speaking French, and so not someone who could connect the snippets that flashed like minnows through the talk. They were the most agile scandalmongers, with years of convent school behind them. They played with lubricious explanations till Aunty Leila pulled them up. "You shouldn't talk like that! When I was a girl I hardly left the house. I feared my parents. It was better that way. . . . But yes, I told some lies," she admitted, and, "yes, I agree that men are strict because they themselves feel guilty. . . . Please," it ended up, "I can't hear such things," and her big face clucked with amusement.

But this century's children prattled on.

With Aunty Leila.

Not in their homes.

It was at Aunty Leila's that they tried out the parts they observed so many of their elders playing.

They could be cruel, of course. If they pardoned Sami, principally because he was a man, they withheld all charity from Christiane. The Sheik's second daughter (and his favorite child) Christiane had refused to marry the various suitors that her parents had produced—in the way these things had always been done, until now, perhaps, with this youngest age group. She had even refused to discuss with her mother the sort of man she might find acceptable. She had continued at the American University, piling up degrees and grants. She was a blue stocking, and it reflected on Yola, who had no wish, thank you, to be daubed with that brush. Les Jeunes Filles were up in arms for Yola. How awful to have an unmarriageable sister! One who had done a survey in the brothels. Who had interviewed Nasser for a Muslim paper. Who had a nervous voice. It was such a bad image.

"There is something," they were saying, "in this latest rumor connecting her with Hamid Zoghal. An old wolf like him. Who hasn't been his mistress? How awful it would be for your mother, Yola—no shame at all. At least she should manage not to be seen with him in public. I've heard. . . ."

They had pins into Christiane. She seemed to disturb their self-assumptions far more than the brother Sami.

There was a final thrust, "I suppose that she imagines she is a Lebanese Simone de Beauvoir!"

But remarks like these did not compose all their conversation. They were full of the latest news of parties and of dress designs received from Paris and of films. They were great moviegoers. "Aunty darling, they were kissing like this!" But they held back from the demonstration. "It would shock you, Aunty. I can't wait till this evening to see if Alain knows about it." Laughs. A few dance steps about the room. When they visited Aunty they hitched up their skirts to the mini-length forbidden at home. They were bursting with sex, though coolly determined to see that it got its market value. They kept asking Aunty Leila's advice about this or that prospective man. She always said, "Why ask me?" But they liked to ask her, to tease her a little, as indeed they compulsively teased themselves with their talk of other people's orgies.

They were shackled (each father's honor was at stake), but they were cavorting gaily inside their shackles.

Raoul commented, after they had gone, "You should see them when they think they are alone! They play the most obscene games. Certain dances, you know. And their conversation is the detail of what they have told their priests. Or of what their doctors have had to tell them. Those little beasts are not so innocent." He would not say more, though many people talked of the pranks on skiing parties. The driven snow had cause for blushes.

Their attitude to Christiane was mean.

But then she sounded emancipated.

Raoul preferred it when they did not come. It enabled him to be even more scathing in conjecturing what they might be doing under their Aunty-from-Egypt's umbrella. He pretended that Yola was corrupting the chauffeur. He particularly had it in for Yola. The more innocent she looked, the more like a peach, the more simply affectionate and homely with Leila (and all these girls, at first casual look, had an unspoilt, homely charm), the more unbelieving grew his face and the more insidious his comment. He provoked Yola into boasting foolishly. He was a wily devil. Raoul was a man who would have made an expert interrogator.

Leila did not like this, but she suffered it because her brother was her dearest love.

And after her brother and her son in America, her next love was for Sheik Nassib.

What did Raoul do with his evenings? He went out quite often alone. Once a week they had a dinner party; and he and Leila were invited together to the perpetual run of Hadiri gatherings. Leila sometimes went to the church, and from there, with cousins, to Sheik Nassib's. But otherwise she watched television (she never missed Abu Melhem and Abu Salim, the Arab comedians), and she instructed Hoda in sewing her trousseau, and she saw that supper was there for Raoul when eventually he did come home. He got invitations to all kinds of functions, foreigners especially seeking him out because he had this reputation as a poet. He said that he hated cocktail parties but would just look in to see who was there, and then when she asked him, "And who was there?" he said, "Oh no one, no one." One wondered if he had actually been. On one such evening I had seen him lurking, not at the German Institute, as supposed, but in a side street close to the cabarets. He had had the air of a practiced poacher in the field. He had looked sadly alert, about to punish himself. He must have had some quarry there, some need that he had to satisfy.

One evening I asked him, at the close of a visit that had lingered on from four o'clock, "Are you doing anything this evening? Would you care to go to a cabaret? Personally, I go for the belly dancers."

He laughed at the taste. "You should go to Damascus. Do you remember Badia in wartime Cairo? But I'll take you to one that is not too bad. About midnight then. Have a snooze first."

We set off between midnight and one. We avoided the international cabarets, though a European turn, say a strip-teaser, or chorus girls with a Cockney grimace bashing out the old routine, were required parts of a Beirut show. We went to a shabbier sea-front establishment, which nonetheless was packed to the door. There was a man already singing on the stage.

Raoul had a way of silencing the pimps who clustered on the pavement, sailors' friends every one of them; and he summoned the manager and with literally a word secured the placing of an additional table up against the stage, to one side. A whiskey bottle was set upon it. The manager slid us into our seats. The singer, lost within his song, had broken off on the dominant note, resting himself while the impas-sioned players thumped their drums and raced their fiddles, but he found time to greet us with a wave before, gold teeth blazing, the Egyptian *rababe* or two-stringed fiddle leading him into the new mode, he embarked upon the most intricate phrasing, his hands fluttering with the nuance of the story, his face laughing as he trilled the melody, broke off, trilled it again and again, then climaxed with an extended note that threatened to split open his cheeks. He broke off as suddenly. The *kanun*, the zither, took his song to its conclusion.

"Pretty poor," said Raoul. "We haven't come for that." And he also dismissed the two slinky girls that the manager had sent toward us. "And I didn't come for that," he commented after the next singer, a coquette, thin in voice and even thinner in figure, had wiggled her hips and let her shoulder strap fall and reacted to applause by kneading her breasts as she cried forth broken notes of suffering.

The audience, nearly all of it male, drinking whiskey and, at the back, beer, fizzed with excitement in the semi-darkness, a condition to the profit of the management's girls, who, planting themselves wherever they could, topped up the glasses. These girls were a pretty low class of whore but toward them, in public, the Arab male—from villages, and over from Syria, some of them—displayed a most finicky etiquette.

"Ah now!" For at last, after one more turn, by (charitably) a French comedienne, one of the big singers was announced. New musicians had come on stage. Their instruments as usual comprised, on the extreme left, two four-stringed fiddles termed *kemendjah*, tuned by fifths; next, the *kanun*, placed on the knees, a modern version of David's harp, whose strings could be plucked with incredible rapidity by quills fixed to first and middle fingers. The *kanun* player was the leader of the group. On his right came first the *konitra*, the lute; then the *gosba*, the flute, the instrument that gave each change of mode to the singer; then lastly the tambourine and a *derbakki*, side drum. We were sitting close up to these drummers. We were fortunately spared kettle-drums. No sooner were they there than the *derbakki* player placed his drum beneath a low-standing lamp, on top of which went the tambourine. The idea was to tighten the skins.

On came the singer. What applause! Her name was cried with a string of compliments, one man outdoing another. She stood there, hands to the microphone, adjusting it beneath her face, which was geisha-white and fat and sulky, ignoring the opening beats of the musicians, her huge body, which looked as if it had broken the springs of every bed it had lain on, zipped into a glittering gown. That gown was tight as a diving suit, with a black satin base covered with glittering gold and silver tassels. Her high-heeled sling-backs glittered too. She stood there glittering and looking discontented, and when finally she threw in some notes, taking over from the flute's introduction, they were perfunctory, a sort of rehearsal in her mind, and once again she was adjusting the microphone. She tossed her hair, an untidy mane. Then she actually smiled, a private grin, at some leering word of the *kanun* player.

She turned toward him, then, with more confidence, let forth a piercing cry, trilling it, embroidering it within her nose, then letting it go in a fade-away drawl. One could see from where flamenco came. This pleased her slightly; she gave a kick at the cable trailing from the microphone, and she offered the audience a first, faint shimmy, a grotesque pointer to what her body could do. A corner of the scarf hanging from her shoulders found its way, demurely, to her mouth.

Suddenly she was with us. She had sung the first theme; paused, coughed, stared at her sling-backs as if to make sure they were the matching color; then she had carried us into a secondary theme with a sudden gift for elaboration that

"The Phoenician spirit had subtly prevailed, infecting all who came to this coast." *Directorate General of Antiquities, Beirut*

"The mountains . . . a refuge for minorities, in particular for the
Maronite Christian community." *John Sykes*

"The center of Beirut glowed, and looked solid." *CNT Beirut*

The music had quickened. The drummers seemed demented. The *derbakki* player had a long, thin neck thrusting to and fro like a snake. The tambourine was jingling and exploding. The *kanun* player was bent almost double, teasing an extra twang per second. The stage rippled. Then on came the dancer, light and fast in an arc past us, her bare legs stretching stilt-like, stretching and bending in a tiptoe run. Her legs, as she ran, were swinging her sideways, legs crossing over, stomach beginning to oscillate at a faster rhythm, to quiver and quake, to jump at us, till her whole person was quivering headily like a pot finally come to the boil.

She circled the stage. She had a proud face. Her eyes laughed with temperament, and each limb was contending to get ahead; but, subject to the measured beat of the drums, she cracked that right leg into play, kicking it out and out, and out, with the folded-back skirt shimmering on the hip, and the undulations of her stomach unceasing. She turned and took a running chassis or two as she flung her hair wild behind her, then settled, lowering her body slightly, into an even faster movement, as first her front and then her back spun like a top while her feet advanced with little ecstatic stamps of their own.

She stopped. She was facing the tambourine player, who had a big, bald, middle-aged head. Sticking out her bottom, she awkwardly kissed him, in parody of some wicked child; then she sat on his lap; then she removed her outer skirts, and scarf, and draped them over his shoulders. It was her joke. It delighted the audience. It delighted her. She went quivering away, looking back with little grins of pleasure, tossing her head at the ribald comment thrown out by the *kanun* player. Then she was slowing, pawing the ground anew, then sinking onto wide-spread knees.

She was close to a table. She fixed her gaze solely on the men sitting there. She began a slow pelvic roll, around and had the *kanun* player speeding his fingers as if they were a thousand May flies.

Applause. She was actually beginning to like us. Her monstrous shape shook suggestively. Her hands went to smoothing it down. Then, singing again, she caressed the mike in an agony of tender pain, her voice jerking out a little phrase that for some moments she was simply repeating— to roars from the men, then a grin from her, and the beginnings of a lewd ripple through her body; and then she was singing with a fast, free rhythm, embellishing, and, with every cheer—as her eyes shot to the left and right—emphasizing the further variation. The song seemed to be going on forever. "She is good," said Raoul. "All she is saying is that she would like her lover to play with her a little, just to show that he likes her a little."

It was obvious that she was being explicit.

Afterward, she sang other songs: about how it was sweet to be in the garden; about how she would serve him a cup of coffee before the horseman mounted his charger. She certainly knew her public's taste. By now she was giving shimmies by the dozen; in those intervals of rest when she turned to the players and threw them a cough or a word or two, her backside, like an enormous moon, continuing to salute the audience. Then once again she launched a little phrase, a little arrangement of quarter tones, which, as she brayed and crooned and nearly choked with emotion, she reworked, and reworked, until we all seemed to have been sucked into her, so overwhelming had become her presence. Then she released us with a few delicate quavers, and the abrupt end came.

She waddled off without a backward look. Further applause had no part in it.

"At last your dancer is coming on."

"His subject was the Muslim-Christian dialogue." *ODS Beirut*

"Preoccupied with having a good time in the process of being lined up for husbands." *CNT Beirut*

"You are always somebody else's poor." *ODS Beirut*

"The Arab heart is the biggest in the world!" *ODS Beirut*

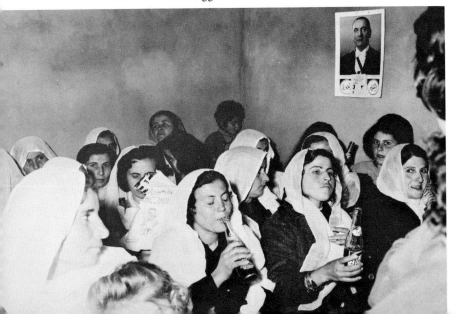

"To make the calculations and adjustments, as with all Lebanese
at lightning speed, that would hand him some new advantage." *Casino of Lebanon*

"He would not say more, though many people talked of the pranks on skiing parties." *CNT Beirut*

"There is an immense task of education—of communication, as Americans term it." *ODS Beirut*

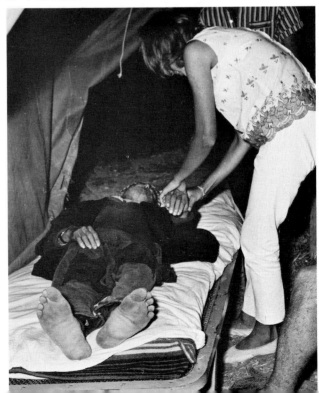

"Lebanon's educated middle class—most of it Christian—is her basic wealth." *CNT Beirut*

" 'I particularly love the Biqa,' said Maurice . . . 'It is dry and one sleeps well at night.' " *CNT Beirut*

"There was the same kind of hopeless refuse." *John Sykes*

"The mettlesome man who had defied the Turks during the later nineteenth century."
John Sykes

Earlier it was Fakh al-Din's capital, and for other Ma'n and Shihab princes." *John Sykes*

"In this Holy War we shall spare no Jew." *John Sykes*

" 'All the same, be wary after dark' . . . 'When the truth gets around, there'll be a hot reaction.' " *John Sykes*

"Arabs were gentlemen. The question was, were the Jews gentlemen? Were the Americans or the Russians gentlemen?" *ODS Beirut*

"I am working for a new society." *ODS Beirut*

"We are the beacon of Christianity in Asia." *John Sykes*

around; then she swooned backward, her head on the floor, but her front part turning, oscillating, then bucking at them in simulation of venereal delights. A tease, she moved on, from table to table, varying these down-to-earth exhibitions, as a man with a lasso might, each time, vary the way he swung and uncoiled the rope. She clicked her bottom from side to side, responding to the exact crack of the drum. She shook her breasts, her hair, her hands in a sudden frenzy of recollection. She came unexpectedly, at the fifth table, on an American lady entranced by her performance; and the two of them, for some minutes that followed, seemed lost in an orgastic dream of their own, slow smiles covering their features as the dancer, very close to the guest, re-enacted all those movements, a revelation that tickled the assembly. Alas, she did not continue to us, for the rhythm changed. She followed its magic, she strove and kept in step with its beat as the drummers speeded up to their maximum. Flashing, cracking, lilting, swaying, as though now driven by a thousand devils, she sidled and kicked and whirled about the floor. Her magnificent body came proudly through.

"Are you satisfied?"

"And how!"

"In Egypt my father sometimes had them at home, dancing, you know, on the occasion of a birthday. Oh look, there's Hamid!" His gaze, swinging round in this moment of complete relaxation, caused him to speak in the same instant. I turned, and some tables behind us to the right was Hamid Zoghal in a party of six, among whom was the girl whose hand he had held momentarily at the charity ball.

"Who's the tall girl?"

"Oh? That's Christiane. I was forgetting that as yet you haven't met her." Suddenly Raoul looked a shade displeased. He seemed to withdraw his confidence from me. "It would seem to be a journalistic party." He turned back from it;

but when the next number started, a Greek singer with accompanying guitar, he said quickly, "Could we slip out?"

In the street, he began discussing America. All his sardonic friendliness was back.

Father and Son

The season for public holidays had started, so people were often not in their office. Then I flew over to Jerusalem for a week, returning by a relay of service-taxis to Amman, then Damascus, then over the mountains in a thick, flashing deluge of rain at speeds that not even a sniper's bullet could have hoped to interrupt. We survived. With political tensions rising fast, each frontier became stickier to negotiate. One forgot the mere hazards of motoring.

A day later, the tenth of May by now, I went to Sheik Nassib's office. He had been inquiring about me, and the moment I rang, his secretary made an appointment. There was a brisk simplicity to the telephone call that was repeated on his business premises. We were five storys high overlooking the port, and the clamor of cranes and shouts of porters—at the heart of Beirut's entrepot tradition. And all who worked in the Hadiri building, greeting and assisting the arrival of a visitor, obviously reflected their efficient chief. Though also a Deputy and the head of a clan, here primarily he was the managing director. New York, São Paolo, Milan, Tokyo, and other centers, wired to his person, helped to keep the office lively.

"I am pleased that Madame Shemegh could find you an

apartment. Better so, I think? You have just come from
Jerusalem?" He waved me to a club armchair and to cigarettes
and a soft drink; then he was back at his desk, again taking
the phone. He closed the mouthpiece. "All the Lebanese
are keen travelers. We surpass the Greeks." He continued
his call, buzzed his secretary, added a second, complementary
call. His broad face worked without expression, though his
voice was like plasticine adapting to the shape the conversations required. He was not an Arab who wasted words, in
this role of international merchant. He listened well, then
made decisions. The calls completed, he told his secretary to
bring in some pamphlets.

These pamphlets he had collected for me. They comprised
every travel brochure on Lebanon, and social welfare bulletins,
trade reports, souvenir programs from Baalbak festivals, and
articles copied from foreign magazines—the kind of material
that rarely one would look at except when waiting one's turn
in a queue. The Sheik was now pressing it on me with his
affably gentle, iron-tough manner, saying, "It will help the
book that you should write. We want the world to know.
It is a country for tourists—and not simply while on their
way to Jerusalem. Later I will take you myself to the
mountains. Dear sir, for your book!"

I was taken aback. I was still studying Islamic themes and
not seeing how they made a book. In fact it was now, facing
him and the bold intelligence of a mountain chieftain come
down to conquer the city, that the seeds of a book began
to stir.

As usual I was slow. This was only his prologue. Deviously,
by way of the "Lebanese soul," the "treasured customs,"
the "picturesque ruins" so pleasant to visit on summer picnics,
he got round to saying, "What you should realize is that
we are a well-run country. You will doubtless have heard
other reports. But, my friend, just think of what you observed

in Damascus as you were coming through. Do they have enough food as we have? Is there enough food in Egypt?"

While making this point he was brooding a little, perhaps thinking of some business affair. Almost mechanically he went on, "We have good laws, good institutions that have evolved over a period of time. Who is so mad as to throw them away? This is a country of free speech and of a free press. You worship freely. It is a small but very liberal country, and, with the exception of Kuwait, the most prosperous economy in the Arab Middle East. Sir, that is due to free enterprise. We are not shackled by too much government, as in Egypt or Syria. We are more relaxed."

Halting to answer the phone once more, he came back quickly. "Your Mr. Heath keeps crying, 'Set the people free!' Sir, we are free. That is the secret of the Lebanese economic miracle."

I asked him about the Intra crash. Hadn't that been due to too much freedom in the realm of banking and business practice? Didn't it mean that the flow of money from the oil sheikdoms, so vital to Lebanon, would faster than ever begin to turn to investment in America and Europe?

He smiled. "Yes, yes, for the moment, perhaps, we are a little short of capital. My brother Badri could explain this to you. Some bankers, and Yusuf Beidas was one, sometimes— er—cannot find the cash. Frankly, sir, we are better without him. But, as the service center for the Middle East, Beirut will quickly recover. We have very alert, educated men. Lebanon's educated middle class, most of it Christian, is her basic wealth. Please, I beg you, have confidence in us!"

His hands were raised with the fingers splayed out in that typical Mediterranean gesture. He was smiling playfully, enjoying the role of seeming to ask me for understanding. For he, after all, was the man of power. And yet he did want something from me, and not, I now felt, the tourist book.

We smiled at each other. I felt absolutely sure that it was he underwriting the nominal rent for which Leila had given me the apartment.

Perhaps it was just inherent in him, and in so many Lebanese, to set the stage for getting something from one before he had even decided what it was.

He was saying rapidly, "To understand the country, there are one or two people that I think you should meet. They have served us well. May I arrange it?"

I readily agreed. In this way I met ex-President Chamoun, the two Eddé brothers, and the Kataeb leader, Pierre Gemayel —Maronite leaders who had held high office. They may have placed their emphases differently, but, good Maronites all, their understanding was in close sympathy with Sheik Nassib's.

This interview at his office had to end because the phones were jumping again and this was about the time he could allow to any one visitor. "Ah!" he cried, "I am coming with you too! I have just been called from the house." He put down the phone, canceled all arrangements, and a few minutes later we were going down the lift. Close up, I could admire the quality of his suit. He was groomed for a royal audience, yet he kept this slight edge of roughness as though, if you challenged him, he could fell a tree or build a wall as fast as any farmer, and perhaps it was deceptively reassuring. "Good luck, I am told, is on the way for my constituents. The President has been gracious enough to listen. Remember, Lebanon is a democracy in which the President is almost a king. Almost. As in the USA. And of course, constitutionally, he is always a Maronite. That, sir, we can never part with!"

His smile, enigmatic, seemed at last to convey something in which he was supremely interested.

One could feel the brush past of ambition.

I accepted his invitation to lunch a week later.

In the meantime I went to Robert's office. The procedure here was totally different. There was a squad of porters at the desk downstairs to check visitors, but they waved one past, too intent on their gesticulating argument. In the elevator there was a man with a tray of Turkish coffees, steaming fresh, for the floors above. Robert, as the Director General of the Ministry, was on an upper floor at the end of a corridor, through the doors of which one could see his assistants, drinking coffee and chatting if they were women, staring morosely at space if they were men. Mountains of paper rested on their desks. From behind the only door that was closed, screams of rebuke and sobs could be heard. At the end was a long conference room and the office of the private secretary, and beyond that the DG's office. The Minister worked on the floor above.

I was asked to wait in the conference room (as the DG had not yet arrived), through a door of which, leading into her office, I could watch the private secretary. She ordered me a coffee, and the coffee men appeared. There were five other men waiting in the room, but only two of them had been offered coffee. The other three did not resent this, but sat with ingratiating smiles, one fiddling with his beads and winking with jokes. The two who had coffee were reading their papers and exchanging an occasional subdued word. Another man appeared, gave us each a little bow, and for the secretary a lower bow and smile of polite resignation, and he sat modestly quite a way down the room. He had the marks of a regular petitioner.

The secretary herself was served a second coffee, and, reading her paper, she smoked continuously, emitting the smoke in gusty clouds. We all patiently watched those clouds, conscious that there was a determined girl making her way against tradition. Her phone kept ringing, and whereas she spoke to messengers and petitioners in Arabic, her phone conversations were invariably in French; and one gathered that they were mostly to other private secretaries at other Ministries in an exchange of news and of working favors for particular clients. In that way all things were arranged by this well-placed circle of girls. I was to confirm this when visiting other Ministries, waiting in little groups of petitioners where I had not sought any special entrée, but was there really to savor the scene: one of the last old touches of the Orient.

(I remember, for instance, once in the Egyptian Delta, I think it was at El Mansourah, calling on some local governor . . . "Come in, my dear"—or was it friend or brother? He was an exuberant man, using flowery speech, and he placed me there among the special petitioners—those whom he would be seeing that day—on a long bench facing his desk, and he was most fastidious about the coffee. Other petitioners crowded the passage and the courtyard, and occasionally a policeman was sent out to silence the noise, which he did energetically with a thick stick. The governor kept me waiting in order that I should admire his performance. I had a front seat, and each time he came around his desk to box a petitioner's ears, the crack and the slap went down one's spine. Pow! as they say in the comics. Zonk! With other petitioners he patiently argued, with some he was sugary, with others bored. Eventually he would see every one of them without delegation to a lower official. In the meantime, patience, words, blows, as the hot fly-blown day ticked by.

(I am assured that it is the same under Nasser.)

At last Robert arrived and I left the group growing in the antechamber. He waved me to a chair with his father's gesture (he was somewhat taller than Sheik Nassib, with an athlete's jauntily dressed figure, yet with his official's decorum also), and he questioned the girl about the petitioners. He went out to them and satisfied three with a few quiet words. He ignored the others and closed his door. He made one phone call in high-pitched Arabic.

"So sorry. Excuse me." He was a westerner again. "I had

to go to a special meeting. Things are far more serious than is said. Do you intend staying on in Lebanon?"

"Yes. Have the Israelis attacked Syria?"

"They are speaking of it." He blinked, grew bland. "This is always a turbulent area."

"My feelings are"—again his tone changed, brushing yet more of what he knew out of sight—"that we must concentrate on our internal problems. I imagine Dr. Zoghal said this to you. It is the way to be strong, to contain the Israelis, and in the long run, in the Middle East area, to absorb them in our wider Arab culture. You would not, of course, read that in the papers. But it is, I submit, the practical view"— he laughed—"and only intellectuals hold it!"

"You see," he urged, "here in Lebanon, how can we cling to a fragmented society—upheld by the National Pact, etc.— and fit into the twentieth century? I am sure if you have talked to my father and his friends you will have heard their defense." He smiled decorously, the youthful lawyer still active in him. "They will have decried my technocratic views!"

"But seriously," he urged, "I am perfectly aware of the defects in our government machine. Take civil servants. Well, there are three generations: those of seventy, who served the Ottomans, those of fifty, who served the French, and my crowd, in their middle thirties, who are trying to create something Lebanese. Not, you will notice, advantageously Christian or advantageously Muslim, but Lebanese. Since 1958 we have overhauled the system. Well, we have made a beginning. There is still the fight between the three generations; and still Christians who favor Christians or refuse to delegate authority to a Muslim. And vice-versa. It will need a generation to weed out the fifty percent of our staffs who should not be in the service any more. Even so. . . ."

He paused. We lit cigarettes.

"Even so," he continued, "time is short. The world is

changing rapidly about us. We can't wait for the perfect machine before we assume our responsibilities. And that is where I differ from my father."

"I differ from him," he politely repeated, "though I don't demean the excellent work done by men of his generation. They cast off the French; they made our State an internationally accepted affair. But we remain unstable. Our so-called freedom is an anarchy we cannot afford. The State has to take over from the chieftains—who also include our entrepreneurs—and lay out a more ordered society. In brief, I mean, we must enforce taxation; we must control the banks and investment policy; we must provide the main countrywide services and not leave them to the patronage of Deputies. We must especially see that the mass of young Muslims, as they become better educated, do not in despair turn to Communism, or to any loyalty except Lebanon, but fairly, through merit, find their place in the expanded State enterprises. For don't imagine that private business or the private transactions of our politicians will see to that in time. Time, monsieur, is the essence of the problem."

He summed it up: "We have to transform Lebanon into a modern society."

"Like all the other new states? Aren't there dangers? You know, through over-centralization?"

He considered it gravely, then shrugged his shoulders. "Yes, a regional bias has its points. People do more easily participate. Face to face. I can hear my father saying it. But . . . we have to change! If you saw it from inside . . ."

He smiled. "If you only . . . saw it from inside!"

"I suppose you feel sure that your Muslims will eventually accept a secular state. As in Turkey."

"Absolutely sure. In ten years' time we could have a Muslim President and risk nothing. That would be the crux. But what a relief to be done with confessionalism!"

"In ten years' time?"

"Well, in twenty, in thirty. Our job is to lay the foundations." He looked at his watch. "The morning has gone. Shall we go for an Arab luncheon?"

With a flourish as though concluding a Divan, and again revealing the athletic figure that in his case owed less to the Mountain than to years of tennis and riding in France, he cast aside official routine and swept me out to his chauffeured car. Strong in theory, he seemed to bother less about those humbly bowing petitioners than would a man of an older generation. For him they stood for the feudal psychology. He offered a modern broom.

Raoul was to laugh when I told him later about Robert's Arab luncheon. "He's the most French of us all when it comes to eating. His snails are flown out from Bourgogne. Their chef is from Paris. Of course his wife, Wadad"—and here came one of Raoul's twitches—"is so indecently rich, he can go for what he likes, including his near-Marxist ideas. They may be required for our mongrel society. But never forget his Orthodox wife's immense fortune or, additionally, her pro-Syrian sympathies."

"Is that what helps him to oppose his father? Being financially independent?"

Raoul laughed. "In his case, no. Robert's strength is intellectual. And we have yet to see, when it comes to the crunch, that Robert will oppose his father!"

However that might be, the luncheon was splendid, a feast of Near Eastern delicacies. I chose, because I had liked it of old, a potage of *moulōukieh:* gluey-green, garlic-drenched, the rice and the chicken slipping down, but the taste of the herbs sticking to one's teeth, nostalgically, through the afternoon. Robert had chicken stuffed with nuts, but only after a prolonged analysis, with the head waiter, of each alternative. He chose a French wine. We had a huge hors d'oeuvre, a meal in itself, with *hammus bi thini* (mashed chickpeas in sesame oil) in a dish into which we both dipped our bread, a practice inducing a camaraderie not awakened in theoretical discussions. Even so, I couldn't get closer to Robert. I felt he was right, but not congenial.

His father, on the other hand, was congenial, and by the same token possibly wrong—wrong, that is, in his entrenched ideas.

He had heard that I had been lunching with Robert, but he did not at first refer to this. To Leila's delight he sent his car to her apartments to pick me up. His nephew Maurice, who was Badri's son, with a finger in the bank and also in the business, and also in their cousin Farid's factory—for among these quicksilvery gentlemen, Maurice was seemingly the slickest of all, and brilliant, where Sami was a fool—was in the car, and so we met. And he said, as we dropped him off at his house in the next street to the Sheik's residence, "I am to see you tomorrow if you accept the Sheik's offer. He thinks the factory will interest you. It is more the kind of coming venture in a mercantilist country like Lebanon."

He didn't wait to ask if I could manage it. That lay in his uncle's hands.

And who would think of refusing the Sheik?

The gates opened by remote control (the high walls were also wired, and there were dogs and this bodyguard-chauffeur ready to stave off intruders, and Raoul swore there were enough arms hidden to deter all but the regular army), and the car drew up before an elegant mansion with a long frontage of decorative glass and stone volutes shaded by trees, and something of the interior richness streaming out into the sunshine. There were treasures there. A male secretary led me to a corner of the hall, which was flashing with marble and a mosaic inlay—lifted, I was later informed, from Palmyria. And there were pictures, pennants, armor hanging as in the abbey of a medieval order; and Arab chests and wrought iron dishes, and in the far corner, catching the light coming in from the leafy garden, a low-mounted kneeling statuette, in alabaster, of an Egyptian king. That had been dug up here? Secretly transported?

No time to wonder, for a door was opening and Sheik Nassib was hurrying forward, extending an arm that in the same movement pressed one down into an easy chair next to the cocktail tray.

"My wife."

She had approached so silently from some other direction. She had a sharp, infinitely gracious face, schooled, one would say, to play her part in the thousand and one ventures of her husband, without reckoning them too important. With her, following, it seemed, a shade after, was a glow of otherworldly conviction. She was not involved in the museum about us. She chatted easily for a few minutes, hinting at other dimensions of being, then as silently withdrew. And she could be heard in a gallery over our heads calling softly, and there was an answer of rustling convent skirts. The Sheik waved me on to the dining room.

This room opened on a courtyard, small, marbled, with a fountain playing, enclosed so that the light streamed in, as in a *hammam*, through the curved roof studded with goblets of colored glass. There were wall screens of floral design, hand-painted and enameled, and corner basins whose spouts were formed from the mouths of Roman lions. In the room itself, which had other windows overlooking the garden, what wall remained was of wood paneling, illuminated with Kufic writing. There were hanging lanterns. There was a showcase, softly lit, with a collection of millefiori plates and some figurines, later established as tiny bronze Hittite gods. There was a rich carpet, and open on a lectern, as though for a suitable reading during lunch, was a lavishly illustrated copy of Lamartine's *Voyage en Orient*. The Sheik, one could see, was himself still a traveler, ransacking the past for the present.

A male servant waited on us. A usual main dish, a fish *sayyadieh*, of bass fillets and onion puree, set around rice covered with pine nuts, was a starter here. There were steaks afterward with french fried potatoes and salad; then lemon sherbet. The Sheik was not a man to read a menu when favorite food could be on its way. He ate lustily. He did not drink alcohol. As in all things, he was a man in a hurry, and afterward, showing me over his collections on both floors, through rooms and galleries, and outside in the tropical garden (artificially heated if the temperature fell), he gave the impression that he had put them together through agents' advice or in spare half hours, here in Beirut, or traveling in the area, or on business trips to western countries. Little more than had seemed his wife was he involved with them. They were a part of the levantine panoply of power.

He said: "My ancestors were farmers in Bisharri. Some were priests—though never bishops. We were thorns in the side of the ruling clan. When the Maronites began spreading south, in the sixteenth and seventeenth centuries—during the time of Fakhr al-Din, who was a great emir and a friend of the Christians and also a friend of the Tuscan Medicis—we moved south. My family prospered. Some were still priests, and some were monks who built monasteries and themselves farmed and brought education to the poorer people. Our community would not have grown strong as it did if it had not been for that religious enterprise. We are a people still close to our Church.

"Yes," he continued, "it was not till the time of that other great emir, Bashir . . . Bashir the Second at the start of the last century . . . that one of the Hadiris became a bishop, and then he almost became the Patriarch! A fighting man who supported the peasantry in casting off their Druze lords. It was a time of change—as again today. There was trade with the towns, trade with Europe. The Great Powers were becoming interested. Lebanon has a most colorful history! You must read it if you wish to write about us."

This thought occasioned a change of subject.

The Sheik managed to eat very quickly, to sit back and rest, and to talk at the same time. He watched me catching up, then asked, "Did Robert convince you of his technocratic notions?" He spoke lightly, but there was a heaviness somewhere.

Without waiting for an answer—his Lebanese way, with the speed of lightning, was to guess one's thoughts, to hold up a hand to represent them, then continue arguing against that hand—he spat out, "They are not paid enough. They lack expertise. They have no initiative. Civil servants cannot run a country! Are we, dogmatically, to blind ourselves and give that system more authority? At the same time to destroy the freedoms slowly won over fifty years? No sir, to progress, run slowly."

I repeated what I thought was a vital point: that surely the young educated Muslims, not just scions of leading families, must win a fair stake in the country if Lebanon was to be secure? Perhaps only the State could insure that possibility?

"Of course, of course"—but he was a politician—"I entirely agree. But there are many ways of bringing that about. My nephew Maurice has interesting plans. We are working more with Shia families from the south of Lebanon who are entering business. On our boards we all sit with Muslims. I am a great believer in encouraging the Americans, and the British, too, to invest here. That, sir, is the way to make jobs, to meet this rush—if there is a rush—of young, qualified Muslims in Lebanon. As I said before, if they have intelligence, they will work for people who pay them properly. What can they earn from government service?"

He patted my arm reassuringly. "We can't move ahead of traditional loyalties. This country has its own old ways. Robert is a prophet—a Shihabist prophet—of theories and doctrines that only a few intellectuals discuss, among themselves, you understand, in clubs." He was laughing genially. His bushy eyebrows seemed to grow larger and darker. Enjoying himself, he began pushing me forward to view the varied loot he had collected, in one room after another.

"I have had a good report," he said reassuringly, "from one of those friends I sent you to. He thinks that you should meet the President and one or two other personalities. May I arrange it?"

I was only too grateful. But why in the world was he taking this trouble? Was it just out of his own great energy, bounding forward to every opportunity at the speed of pure entrepreneurship, which matched that of field commanders, mad inventors, inspired poets? He was happy doing it. He did it and forgot it, like collecting another figurine.

"So tomorrow," he said, "be ready please. At nine sharp Maurice will collect you."

Once again to his car. To the very last moment, his even, watchful, flexible charm. A strong, dry grip. A sturdy stance.

A contemporary chieftain, still very much afloat.

⚜

The Young Industrialist

Leila naturally told Raoul that Maurice would be taking me to cousin Farid's factory. I had been reporting to her on my visit to the Sheik. Characteristically perhaps, on hearing this, he came to my apartment with the surprise announcement that for the very next day he had planned a picnic; we were going to Rachaya at the foot of Mount Hermon; Jane, the American painter, was coming. All arranged! He was taking the day off.

It was difficult, and he made it more so, to explain about the commitment to Maurice.

"But you should have told me!" His face, expressionless, allowed itself to be cast aside. It hung limp; then gradually, not listening to the repeated explanation, it twisted back to bitter disillusion. He gave a shrug. I was a free agent. I seemed to have become, as he suddenly put it, more of a Hadiri than he was. Beware, though: they would drop me as suddenly as now they were crazily taking me up. Beirutis were quickly bored, with people as with news or investments.

He made it a really painful moment.

By now he had brought it to the point of believing that I too had known about the picnic.

He left, leaving an agonized silence.

Jane, when I rang her, laughed with amazement. She had not heard of any picnic.

Next morning Maurice arrived at nine in his flashing two seater Mercedes. I felt guilty enough while driving away, but the episode faded. One's camera eye was again panning along the streets, taking in, though hardly digesting, the nursery-table mixture of style, the tangle of neon, the mounds of rubble, the swaying, pounding pace of the traffic, and at this hour the jostle of people into the giant office blocks. Maurice cut away up a steep side street, burst on a sector of rural cottages, with mud and dust and the squawking of hens, that tenaciously had gone on existing beneath the gaze of city tenements. He entered the main mountain road, which pointed to the outlying strip of orchards and new suburbs and the dazzle of traffic streaming down from the pass to Damascus. He again cut away by a cemetery lane and one of those simple, flat-roofed churches with square belfry that cluster on the Mountain and suggest this would be a Maronite district, a jigsaw piece labeled Maronite (next to others labeled Sunni or Druze or Shia or Catholic Armenian or Orthodox) to be fitted into the map of Beirut.

He passed the French hospital and the army barracks. At the edge of gardens, with a stream flowing, and the shell of the old proprietor's house with its outside stairway and summer shade—so that one could imagine we had come here for vegetables dug fresh out of the soil—he took a track to a high running wall and followed that to an iron gate. Looking back, one got a different view. The gardens had shrunk. The city was close. There were other walls surrounding compounds, with machine sheds and warehouses showing. It was a small industrial neighborhood. Here was the factory.

He had been explaining a few things. He had a Harvard degree. Possibly he should have been a scientist, but his father had wanted him back in the bank. He had this itch to see goods manufactured; it didn't matter what, so long as there was a market and the capital there to buy the machinery. He loved the sound of a new machine starting up a new operation.

Fortunately—in their family—his uncle Nassib handled the marketing, along with cousin Michel and Elie, and Chafiq in the Gulf (who had married Amale, the Sheik's oldest daughter). Then his father, of course, ran the family bank, with himself and Michel's son, Georges, assisting. Sometimes the younger men changed about. With a new venture it was largely a matter of who had time and the most keenness, and, possibly to keep them in order too, his uncle Nassib decided everything. He himself had been sent to cousin Farid to accustom the workers to some new machinery. It was such expensive machinery that one could not chance any negative attitudes. After that, he had other commitments.

The gate, resembling that of a fort, ground open, and we drove inside. The ensemble of buildings did not suggest anything on a large scale or very modern. My most recent visit to a textile plant had been in Scandinavia. Here, with rubble and refuse around, and a lavatory smell, one could not believe that fine cloth was being woven. Maurice, quick to every nuance in the air, answered my thought: "We do bread and butter lines. Household linens, peasant fabrics. We can undercut your country in Africa. There is a demand there for military shirting. The Gulf wants socks. If Farid was willing, we could double this plant within the year."

"How do you cope with the terrible humidity?"

"Like anyone else." He smiled as if to say, "Who the devil do you think we are?"

"Come and look inside."

He had made his point at once. The dirt and rubbish were only in the courtyard, where God still seemingly willed it; inside, conditions were controlled by expensive equipment. The machines, too, were of recent design.

But there were other snags.

"Ah, at last you are here!" It was cousin Farid, in a white mill coat, his ferociously firm face confronting us. "This damned machinery! You should have arranged for an engineer to come from Switzerland. That is how it was done last time."

"We could do that again if something is wrong."

"Wrong? No. I have seen to that. I am a qualified engineer and not ashamed to soil my hands." He addressed me, "Good day to you, sir. In Lebanon, you know, it is considered shaming for a gentleman to soil his hands. But I laugh at that kind of opinion." He struck a sturdy yeoman's stance. "My trouble consists in training managers, who begin by imagining they know everything, to be as unfastidious. Look here"—he called to the man behind him, and gave him a brisk order in Arabic. "I have ordered him to show us his hands. Look at them!" We regarded the manager's hands. "See what I mean? They are too clean. That way the workers don't respect him."

Farid glared proudly down the shed.

"By God, they respect me, though."

He ushered us to the private office, where, for the moment, Maurice also had a desk. He retired to wash his own hands, then rejoined us. Scathingly he called for coffee, as though for once he would bend a principle. In the next office worked two Armenians and two girl typists and a messenger boy—"All I need, thank you," said the owner. "And they not only cope with the mail and the accounts, and what they call research statistics, they assist me with my political work. That's what I mean—this damned machinery! I haven't a moment left to myself."

"Farid, I have good news for you." Between interruptions, pretty constant here, for everyone came to see the boss, Maurice produced papers from his briefcase and showed, with minimum explanation, that a new market was open for the fabrics that the new machinery could profitably produce. Farid lapped it up as easily; but the next instant he was touchy again, complaining that nobody understood all his other responsibilities.

"And what about the workers?" he cried furiously. "I am a philanthropist with regard to the workers. I train them; I make sure their mates are of the same faith and kin. I don't cheat them over wages; I attend their weddings; I pay up when it comes to a funeral. I am father to them. Look at this shed—how bright; look at the taps and basins! And on top of that"—he turned to me—"you must excuse me if you are cousin Robert's friend, but, dear sir, those Shihabist decrees! Don't I already support their families?" He turned to Maurice, "These indemnity payments simply tempt old loyal workers to leave and set up in trade for themselves! Not even our Armenians can think around that one. Damned officials! That's my answer: I can't take more work for the factory because officials have corrupted my workers!"

"Of course, but that is exactly why we are buying you these new machines. To supplant the workers."

"Yes, yes, yes." Cousin Farid understood. But as he switched away to answer a call—coming now, it seemed, from a family group, squatting beyond his office door, who had trekked down from their mountain village to ask about their daughter working with him—he threw up his hands. Was it so easy? Had he not a role to fulfill? Who, finally, understood him?

He later showed me around the compound. It was a well-planned factory. The girls looked neat. Their fingers were nimble, and the cloth was good; the product of so many little teams, of so many little households, almost. Of course, there were far too many operatives, and some of them were just resting and talking, and they smiled at the boss as though he should rest too and add his voice to their discussions. He didn't seem to mind.

His thoughts were elsewhere. "My factory in São Paolo was three times this size. My son Augusto is in charge over there. He will visit me this summer. But I need him permanently. Maurice cannot stay here long. I need my own son beside me."

I knew from Raoul that after the scandal and the affront to the Catholic Lebanese community, Farid had not returned to Brazil. There had been other tragic implications.

His face was proudly stern and gloomy.

In fact, cousin Farid, quite a madman with his pen, and even madder, they said, at political rallies with his cries of "Mission!", "The Sacred Spirit!", "Fatherland!", through all of which he signified the Maronites and their civilizing right to rule this country, looked, when seen close up, as now, to be in personal need of someone to lean on.

Raoul said that women consoled him.

Be that as it may, he continued gloomy once these thoughts of Brazil had struck him. We returned to the office. Maurice, in a mill coat, was studying a detailed plan with the manager. Farid, in no way resenting the authority of this much younger family tycoon, rested a hand upon his shoulder. He looked gloomier still when Maurice announced that he had another appointment in town. We left him looking haughty and forsaken, by almost nobody understood.

"What do you think of it?" Maurice asked me, softly revving his beautiful Mercedes.

"Rather good. I had imagined it would be bigger. Does it pay you to work on that scale?"

"Oh yes. Oh yes. That is Lebanon's way. There are only forty firms in this country that employ over a hundred workers. We talk of a factory, we mean a workshop with ten to twenty-five assistants. The boss or his brother controls each step. It suits us, perhaps. We lack skilled foremen. We wouldn't care for union interference. We can't tie up our limited capital in huge units that your western inventiveness would rapidly make out of date. Of course, if an American offers capital"—he smiled—"as I am in the process of arranging, we are ready to fix up anything he wants."

"You are going in with an American firm?"

"Well, as merchants, we often do that. Now, for manufacturing, I am also proposing—along, just to show you, with a Muslim associate—we shall be, so to speak, a small consortium—to make local perfumes and certain medicines."

"Competing with French and German brands?"

He shrugged. "That is the eternal question. Especially here, with so few raw materials. In this case, though, we do see a profit. To be frank, I get my pleasure from helping to start up one thing or another. I believe you know one of my associates, Dr. Hamid Zoghal. He has been a pioneer in these small new manufacturing enterprises."

"I thought he was a journalist!"

"He is one of the best. He more clearly sees what needs to be done. When a canning factory some years ago was condemned for contaminated material, we started—it was our first joint venture—a small model factory with the very best results. He has also been in school supplies. I see that you are amazed! But, in our society it is only a few people who manage to combine these widely varied interests. You wouldn't find it so strange in England?"

"No. It's a common middle-class trait. So you don't stick behind your confessional barriers!"

"He and I don't, no. You must have talked to Zoghal. Of course, he rather believes in Robert, but the dividend there is a long way off. What can they hope for unless Shihab is reelected in 1970? As Robert likes to say, time is short. It is too short for the State apparatus. Zoghal sees—as we all see—that the young Muslims will become the problem. We are busy creating jobs for them to fill."

"In such small enterprises?"

"All over the country! I have a dozen irons in the fire. Zoghal, and other Sunnis, have more. There are Orthodox willing to put in their wealth. The Shia community, the most depressed of the Muslims, are throwing up men who make money in Africa, then pull it back here into manufacturing. They have leaped the intervening stages. There are also Druzes. But enough of these labels! We are Lebanese. We can perfectly see that the future of our country demands more industry. But, as I say, it will be in small units, at least for two more generations."

We were back in town, in the Raouche quarter. Maurice was meeting Zoghal at the Carlton. I asked him to drop me off before then, but he insisted I should at least join them for a drink. They would not be talking business till later.

It was a pleasure to see the journalist again. In the last moment before shaking hands—although it was he, in the first

place, who had introduced me to the Hadiris—I had the foolish
fear that he would be less friendly. I was so conscious by now
of my attachment to them and that this had distanced me
from the Muslims.

Not at all. His enthusiastic mind immediately dived into
what I had been doing, and he added that I should meet
Christiane (detachedly said) as the one Hadiri who did not
dance to the old Sheik's tune. "Wadad," he went on, "you
know, Robert's wife, is also an anti-Maronite influence." He
laughed at Maurice. "But my dear Maurice, if we don't resist
you at every point, your self-confidence will burn us up. You
Maronites are a full-time problem."

Maurice laughed too. They were two agnostics sharing an
old clerical joke.

Then the atmosphere changed. It changed through Zoghal.
Even when he had shared his news with Maurice, the latter
did not diverge one iota from his smooth, alert, acquisitive
manner (which so excellently went with his white Mercedes),
but Zoghal became impassioned, edgy, then inclined to suspi-
cion, then markedly reserved. Gone, suddenly, his professional
calm and his reasoned sense of priorities. "This will affect us
here," he said. "It could take us back to 1958 if, Maurice,
America takes"—he was cutting the air with the edge of his
hand—"one step to protect Israel and if any of the Lebanese
support that!"

"Hamid, you are forgetting your own editorials, that the
ground on which we win against Israel is, from first to last,
economic. Look at Jordan's progress this year. Look at the
boycott. We are hurting the Jews. Their investment and em-
ployment rates are falling."

"It has happened, Maurice. We must stand to be counted.
It had to come! Now we must win." Zoghal had turned
deathly quiet.

"Are you sure that it is not a trap? Also sprung against
Nasser?"

There was a silence between them—before they hurried on talking—neither of their tones quite so intimate, but the Maronite visibly placating the Muslim, who, whatever toughness his life as a journalist had made a part of him, as an Arab now was uncontrollably moved. The little piece of news that was causing this exchange was that Nasser had asked the UN forces to stand aside from the Gaza border. Egyptian troops were rolling across Sinai. The Cairo radio, heralding support to their "viciously threatened Syrian brethren," was proclaiming Nasser as the Arab warlord. All Arabs must now stand together. The great moment of truth had come.

Back at the apartments Leila was in tears. Raoul, who had been personally to see a friend of his in the Egyptian Embassy, promised her that it was all a big bluff. He was again friendly with me; small things were forgotten. We strove, together with Yola and Lulu—who were perhaps more concerned by the latest assault against two mini-skirted tourists—to calm her down. Why should Beirut suffer? America and the French would protect it.

"Those Egyptians are going to march here," she cried. "They will come through Israel to Beirut and Damascus. Nasser at last really will be Hitler!"

"Aunty, you shouldn't listen to the radio. Let's play a nice dance tune for you." The girls put one on and pranced about.

Raoul grimaced and snapped his fingers. "Aie!" he muttered, "when will Arabs learn? Another flight from unpalatable reality. What putty we become for more ruthless nations." He turned about and lectured the air, "Yet we have so much to give. Out of our deep Arab hearts."

I had heard this often, but not from him. Coming from such a man as Raoul, the words had a beautifully hard ring.

Sheik Nassib never phoned me directly. Even when his secretary phoned, it was to Leila so that I should get the message through one of the family. Now it was Maurice, that same day, who was asked to pass on the information that his uncle had arranged for me to meet the President, that an official car would take me to the Palace at nine the next morning from Robert's office. "I know," he underlined, "it must sound involved, but that's us, if you like. Enjoy yourself! I was thinking, I always go at the weekend to my farm in the Biqa'. It has an 'old world charm.' Christiane, you know, my cousin, often comes. I gather that you haven't met her yet. How's that for Saturday? Good. I'll collect you a few minutes after ten."

Retrospectively, though one was always looking for the intention behind the intention with these people, I don't think there was more to it than that. Christiane often did go there. They had, after all, been childhood companions. Maurice was too unrestrainedly curious not to have kept tuned in to her vagaries. Adaptable to anything, he made the perfect intermediary, and Christiane, among her conformist clansmen, needed some intermediary.

Meanwhile, I met Charles Helou, President of the Lebanese Republic. He was a kind, a very soothing personality, a sort of family doctor risen to the throne, who, between the sharp men surrounding him, seemed best at giving least offense. Beside Karami, Jumblat, Himadeh, Salam, Gemayel, and other politicians, and the controllers within the President's office, the generals, the churchmen, the security chiefs—the daily contenders for the coin of power—he was the one to be labeled Peace. A Shihabist empirically persuaded to go gently with regard to any structural reforms, he conscientiously oiled the machinery, perhaps for the children streaming to the schools (albeit, to schools that continued to divide them) and for adults streaming to the downtown offices (though unemployment was rising rapidly), he was the safest bet for the interim between the savage decade of the 1950's and the certainty of coming struggle in the 1970's. His face, staring from every magazine with the right smile, with his hand of welcome from the right sort of suit greeting some ambassador, was the face that Lebanon was currently assuming. He set the style for the tourist agent, for the public relations man courting investment.

"So how was it?" asked Maurice on Saturday.

"It was a nice idea. You know, your uncle keeps sending me off to these political people. I begin to see why. It's a tactful demonstration of just how much tougher he is."

Maurice was delighted. "I must tell him that one."

"I said it to Leila. Won't she pass it on?"

We were racing up the mountain, the road in places ample enough for eight streams of traffic, four going up and four going down, a motorized survival of the cavalry charge still dear to the Arab heart. Maurice positioned his Mercedes expertly and went through the pack and whined to the bends and swung higher through the wooded escarpments—hazy with mist, where runs of terraces floated out like hanging gardens—and gained the heights, where spring, coming late, still left its color of poppies and crocus and wild lilies among the boulders. And from here, westward, lay the sea, and to the east, the Biqa' and the Anti-Lebanon range, and beyond that were the plains of Syria.

It was nowadays an easy pass to climb, about five-thousand feet, with a daily flow of forty thousand or so vehicles (whose drivers must rarely think back to the muletracks and the narrow bridges and to the first road of 1863, when a diligence from Beirut to Damascus took all of fourteen hours); but it was the sole highway running directly from the port to the West Asian interior. This factor, with a customs mentality at each successive Arab frontier more suitable to the age of brigands, had caused entrepreneurs like the Sheik to invest heavily in air freight. Then by night there were the camel convoys, still following the old tracks, to hustle goods like refrigerators over to Damascus and to bring back gems and textiles or, on a winding southerly course, to take hashish to the smokers by the Nile.

"Have you seen Dr. Zoghal's editorials since Thursday?" Maurice was affecting a rueful grin.

"Yes! Did your business with him prosper?"

"No. Temporarily he had cooled off. Political scares have this effect. He could not risk it becoming known that he would be associating with American capital. He can join later."

"You think the scare will blow over?"

"I am afraid that it suits the Israelis' book. Rumor has it that it also suits the ideas of certain Egyptian generals. Nasser's slide to the left this year may be threatening their place in society. They may be pushing him into an adventure from which he cannot hope to recover. In fact, this escalation looks as though several plots had suddenly met."

"That makes a good footnote to history. So another round of war is coming?"

"Unless America and England intervene."

"England won't. With its memories of Suez. Not even with its present talent for blunder."

"And the U.S. will not be sorry to see Egypt taught a lesson. I fear that the field is open to the Israelis. For them it is the cheapest investment going." Maurice's tone was neutral and inquisitive, that of the alert spectator on the bourse. "Although"—he suddenly corrected himself—"Zoghal seems to believe the opposite. For the moment I think he does believe it. Very little else is in the air! Though it is not like Zoghal." Maurice hugged the ditch as opposing traffic bore against us. Then he slipped ahead and down to the Biqa'.

Indeed, this was the most patent observation: that the usual dispenser of truths on the home front, who was contemptuous of chauvinistic appeal, was suddenly writing like one demented, as his son Ali might have written. Raoul, translating the articles for me, had said that he could not bear to comment. For how explain, from Hamid Zoghal, the cry already of "Arab victory!" and "Israel's ignominious defeat?" "Egypt storms; Israel cowers." This was hardly reasoned language. Like all the press, he was attacking America, whose love for the Jews was fortunately shackled by fear for her oil and by fear of the Russians. Israel knows it is the end, he had written; she is shaking in her shoes. Our guns point down on her. Our armies wait to retake our lands. Our bombers are ready to silence resistance. Even if—and one wondered why he had introduced even this much doubt—there is a shooting war and it lasts for a week, or (surely here just a Zoghal flourish?) even if it lasts for a year, the result is certain: Israel is finished. Again the world will only speak of the people and land of Palestine. At last the great Arab nation will be at peace with all mankind, and will find her destiny.

This being so, he had hastened to add, the Israelis should come to heel quickly. We can still—despite our wrongs—be magnanimous. Our patience however is running out.

"Oh dear, dear," Raoul had muttered, "and this is nothing to the other papers. Only Hamid speaks of magnanimity. Would he, if things went as he predicted, remain so for long? A madness is starting."

He had turned to comfort Leila, only to find her viewing the crisis more philosophically. The very plethora of words on the radio, on television, through a scatter of papers, had dulled her nerves. Perhaps nothing would happen. Too much was being said. Their apartment was still there. The room, the view, the sound of the elevator humming up from floor to floor underwrote continuing stability. "My dear, I want you to try these biscuits. From America!" She had grinned as if, without too much risk, she was teasing us all.

That most virulent article from Dr. Zoghal had appeared

yesterday, replacing his usual Friday pep talk. Today was
Saturday, May 20.

"I particularly love the Biqa'," said Maurice, as we reached
Shtura and turned north. "It is dry and one sleeps well at
night. There's a local wine, and it's away from the city. Noah
is said to be buried here. He probably lived like the Bedouin
now, in a goat-skin tent, grazing sheep. It's high, you know,
here, at a thousand meters; covered in snow all through winter. The valley narrows in the north after Baalbek. I think if I
had been a scientist I should have liked to have done agricultural research"—he flicked the gears through and we sliced a
shadow that a mountain cloud was floating toward us—"in
some such place as this." Then he smiled. "As it is, I make do
with a broiler factory."

One might have guessed that he would have added a factory.
It was tucked away behind his farm.

We turned off the Baalbek road, where the land looked
particularly flat and open with wheat and dairy farming; yet,
almost at once, orchards were gathering, then hemming us in
down a side track. There was a small, dense garden with water
channels and a pool and a trellised arbor, then the house, so
low, and built of the rough stone, that at first its true dimensions were hidden. It looked more like a winter storeplace.
But that was only one façade. Within, in a white-burnished
patio with siesta chairs and plants and carvings and a surround
of shade from wide eaves, one stood at the center of a small
encampment of four such peasant buildings, each walling a
side of the patio, then facing out to the orchards and fields,
and in one direction to some farm sheds, eucalyptus-screened,
and then to the factory. It was not a large factory. It was a
small venture, worked by the family that guarded the place
and cared for the orchards and milked the cows; something
that Maurice was happy to have started. He ran a truck up

from another factory and sold the broilers to a restaurant group in which he had an interest.

There was no one about. There was the large Fiat belonging to his brother Elie. "They must have gone for a walk," he said.

We found them arguing in the doorway of the factory. "It's disgusting," Christiane was saying, and she managed, turning and swinging her nervous voice and her beautiful, thin, nervous figure, to include our approach within her judgment. "Of course," Maurice countered. "What is?" And he folded an affectionate arm about her. He was the younger, by a year, of her two first cousins, but he was far more of a man than Elie. It was odd to see him being affectionate, but then he slid in and out of a gesture.

Christiane liked him. One immediately saw that all that gossip about her and Hamid, whether true or not, was only a part of extremely involved sets of feelings, of the dense, entangled, incestuous play endemic to this sort of society. They all had a call of sorts on one another. Cousin, brother, sister— as endearments, such terms carried sly implications.

She was a beautiful woman, intellectually scornful, and she harped on this as though at some level she also knew it to be a weakness. "Maurice"—half an hour later she was saying— "you know I detest your woolly arguments!"

She was overdoing it. He was in no way woolly. She was simply courting another show of affection.

"Oh, what shall we do?" Maurice was restless. The peasant women had served us a meal of stuffed baby marrows and rice and a mint and parsley salad called *tabbouleh*. And they had been carrying in chicken, but "Not that!" cried Christiane. "Let's forget your concentration camp." And she had asked for another flagon of wine and mostly contented herself with that. She had become more argumentative, but only about words, about teasing trifles, or this or that personality. She seemed to play down her more thoughtful self, but she could

not conceal her eager heart, nor the toll that being "an eccen-
tric" had taken of feminine equanimity.

The peasant had appeared, standing in the shadows. Maurice,
without ceasing to eat heartily, had questioned him in Arabic.
The man had answered shortly, with covert looks at each of
us in turn and at our mode of eating. Then he had squatted on
his haunches and lit a cigarette. "He is a good fellow," said
Maurice in English. "He had sixteen *dunums*. That's four
acres. Now he has added another twenty. I pay him well because he has taught his family the merits of shift work with
machinery. I am lending his brother the money for a tractor
to hire out to neighboring farmers. We are encouraging the
visit of a weekly clinic. We have offered land for a primary
school. Result: his daughter will go to university—after a
thousand years of being peasants—and I, when I stand as a
Deputy for Parliament, will topple the feudal baron here!"

"Oh, not another politician in the family!"

"Who's talking now! Fellow traveler."

"So what shall we do?" He was pursuing his restlessness.
He walked round the buildings, reappearing suddenly. He was
far too smartly dressed for the country. Without his jacket
his monogrammed shirt, with gold tiepin and gold cufflinks,
stood out all the more unhappily. Perhaps he was missing his
business associates with whom he could have advanced some
quiet deal. There was everything here to impress the visitor.
He was itching for more productive talk.

His brother Elie was half asleep with a book.

Christiane was talking to the peasants in the kitchen.

"So what do you say to a look at Baalbek?"

"Not Baalbek again. Please!" Christiane emerged for a moment from the kitchen, then retreated, grinning.

"So what do you suggest? Hasbaya? Shall we view the old
fort where the Druzes butchered a thousand defenseless Christians! I particularly like to remember that occasion . . . with

Madame Jumblat viewing the carnage, the mangled corpses on top of each other, and saying, was it, 'Well done, my Druzes. This is what I expected from you!' In Michigan once I met a Druze, a stockbreeder, whose grandfather—"

"No, not Hasbaya, darling." She had been listening and again appeared for an instant, then retreated, amused.

"So where then?"

In the silence that followed he picked up a paper, let it fall, then retrieved it thoughtfully. "I know what we could do. . . . Listen to this," he said to me. "This paper is two weeks old, but listen to this. But you were there, surely, in Damascus during the religious disturbances? Is that how they appeared to you?"

"I saw commandos with tommy guns cracking the strike in the Suq Hamidieh. They were breaking open shops and removing the goods! I gathered it followed from the Friday sermon and that *mullahs* and priests were being arrested."

"Yes, yes, and no. Things always go deeper. You see, Syria is a terrible country! One has to admit that to 1958 half of the irrigated land was owned by two percent of the people. Of course, absurd"—for Christiane was listening—"of course, there had to be reforms! The feudal servitude was desperate. Not, one might add, much credit to the French, but how do they go about it? They go mad!

"Yes, mad," he insisted, as she began to shake her head, though as yet she was not interrupting, "for one coup has followed another, each bloodier than the one before. The Baath Party—Christiane supported it—sent the best Syrians into exile—to enrich, I might add, the economy of Lebanon. Or it imprisoned them, or left them to the mob. We all know the Syrian mob. How many friends of the family murdered? In unspeakable ways." He smiled at her keenly. "Instead, you see, of fiscal reform and new investment, they expropriated! To be themselves expropriated two months later by the next revolutionary colonel or major, or nowadays it could be a captain! Soon Syria will be run by corporals."

"Who may, at last, be the men," she rejoindered, "to put their country's interest first. Your fat merchants never would have done it."

"Oh my dear, my dear, don't be naïve. Your corporals are good at shelling mosques. Would your care to run over this afternoon and take an unbiased look at Damascus? Come, I'm challenging! There are farms on the way, and workshops that your grandfather helped to establish. My bet is they are wholly ruined."

He returned to me, "Among the present leaders, calling themselves Neo-Baathists, the really tough men—and here is the clue to the steadily worsening ferment in Syria—are Alawites, and Ismailis. You see at heart they are still Assassins, precisely as their ancestors were! They have not lost the appetite for blood. 'Blood-letting,' " he began reading from the paper, " 'makes the best revolutionary medicine.' That's from Jundi, an Ismaili. He heads the Federation of Labor. He is calling for those *mullahs* and Orthodox priests who were arrested to be hanged. 'Death,' it goes on, 'to all reactionaries. Death to those who bring opium to the people!' Christiane, doubtless, would echo that."

She was sugary sweet. "I don't hear you mentioning that those Sunni Sheiks, in their mosques and shops, are for most Syrians the greedy oppressors! The Alawites have for centuries suffered the blows of Sunni overseers. Assassins apart, there are economic explanations for the role that they are assuming now, just as, Maurice, in ten years' time the oppressed Shia peasantry here will come knocking on the rich men's doors."

"No, in Lebanon we shall forestall that with new industries. We have a modern mentality. Surely Hamid has convinced you there?"

"Oh, he's in with you. I am losing faith in Hamid."

"He has been changing course in the last few days!"

"Poof! He merely exposes America for the rampant re-actionary crusader that she is! Israel is America's client. All this year a reactionary wave has been gathering force around the world, and bang, it's suddenly in the Middle East! This little episode you mention in Damascus was engineered by the CIA—"

"Excuse me, you mean by the Alawite strongman, General Salah Jedid! So as to lock up a few more opponents. To terrorize. To placate the mob. Possibly to please his Russian masters. Do you deny that the Russians rule Damascus?"

"Yes, I do. Very well, I accept your bet. Over to Damascus we go. Come! If we don't see a Russian in the first half hour, I think you owe me ten pounds."

"And if we do see one?"

"Oh! You'll have the satisfaction. Come on, Elie." The other brother was awaking. He stood up and mumbled, "I suppose you two have been arguing about nothing. Yes, I vote for going to Damascus. I might just scoop some old jewelry on such a day as this." He glanced at the paper Maurice had discarded. "That atheist affair? Aren't they dull! When they could have had a nice sex scandal."

They decided on the Fiat as being more comfortable, but then Maurice overruled this decision and squeezed us into his car, Elie, who was fat, tucked behind, and Christiane and I at the front beside him. He was in his element again, handling a machine. His restlessness had gone, converted into speed. He ceased to argue. He talked to her differently.

She in turn looked subtly gratified.

The frontier was easy. They no longer seemed to know why exactly they were going to Damascus. Speed and the proximity of the car were enough, with the cool mountain air blowing past. With Maurice at the wheel we were there in forty minutes, swooping over the Anti-Lebanon. As service-taxis approached from the city, he gestured a note of inquiry with his hand, which was outside the car door, turning it up and opening the fingers. At which, in reply, came flaps of reassurance, raised eyebrow nods, more involved hand gestures that told, he said, that Lebanese would be safe but that things were bad for the ordinary Syrian. Press gangs operating . . . house arrests . . . more commando raids against Israel. . . . "But how can you deduce all that?" I inquired. "The most graphic language in the world," he answered. "It seems that the city is becoming a barracks, food rationed, a blackout ordered, but that wise men know that no one will gain from this except the Israelis."

"You made that last bit up!" said Christiane, nestling against him. "You made it up for me."

"Yes, I did, my heart. Please stay realistic."

"But I am. I do not doubt who will gain. I am not Hamid, darling. You know that." She seemed to be saying something else to him. "But that is why I hate the Americans."

"Very well. But that gets none of us anywhere."

"The future," he added, "is America."

Those taxi drivers had gestured the truth. Syria, in utter contrast to Lebanon, was plunged in mournful war preparation. As we sped down the twisting gorge of the Barada, with watery splashes from woods and vineyards and from the miniature scenic waterfalls at the now deserted kebab restaurants, we met truck after truck of abashed peasantry or city youths, guarded by soldiers, being driven away to army camps. Officers in jeeps stormed past, and motorcycle police followed. These police were halting civilian cars (our Lebanese license plates let us through), and we saw men being roughly handled. There was an atmosphere of nervous brutality. Speeding by in our elegant car, we observed with the same remote amazement as we might have observed such events on television.

The gorge opened to the wide oasis, that most enchanted

settlement of gardens and water, with its central mass of suqs and mosques and crisscross of streets concealing palaces. Damascus is a city enclosed in its history, preserved by the deserts and the desert people coming here for what a thousand years has shown them to be an earthly Eden. One has a glimpse from the road coursing downwards, then one is speeding along the gala highway, straight to the Merj, the central square.

Maurice left the car in a garage with a man he knew. There was a rapid conversation. "Now there has been an incident with Jordan! More threats to Hussein. That frontier is closed. We dare not hang about too long. There is a friend I must see. We can drink a coffee. Frankly, at this stage of dementia I should be reassured by the sight of a Russian!"

He whispered cruelly, as we walked, to Christiane: "You who always say that we are Arabs before we are Christians and who say that the Syrians most purely manifest the Arab idea, look about you! Do you like what you see?"

She didn't reply.

Well, the truth was obvious.

Beirut might be a tower of Babel devoted to the commercial idea, with its arrogant banks and limousines, but the street scene there, as we had left it that morning, was also stamped with the thrust for education. Bookshops abounded. Schools of every kind. Eager scholars, even fevered scholars, as though that was the springboard to the modern world and if they did not rush the space would be taken, battled along the crowded pavements. They were enthusiasts, and, of course, Christiane, though older now and more skeptical, was of their breed.

Here we were meeting too many uniforms: drab, slovenly uniforms worn as though the wearer was ashamed or disheartened at being seen wearing it. We met seedy looking soldiers, quarrelsome ones (whom we avoided quickly). We met suspicious officers, officers who dropped their eyes at once, and others, perhaps still in other settings, who were staring soulfully at the crimson petticoats floating in shoals from drapers' stands.

That is not to say that eternal Damascus, with its lilting, mannered conversations and its wiles and graces, had been blotted out, but it had been driven under cover. Even the infinite variety of civilian life had a grey look. There was unease and little loitering. In the cafés men were staring, then whispering. It was as if a great clock had stopped ticking. A pall of fear, of uncertainty, overlay them. "Everyone's talking of war," muttered Maurice. "Poor buggers, they know they're in for it!" Radios everywhere were screeching out slogans between the thump of victory music.

"Oh well, I don't want to stay," said Christiane.

While Maurice and Elie went to see their friend, she accompanied me to the Ommayad Mosque. Suitably garbed, we paced its courtyard. She elucidated a part of the mosaics. The north minaret was caught in sunshine, whereas dusk was gathering below. We squatted inside, but she moved away, saying that was more seemly. She was closed in herself and not companionable.

She was inordinately relieved to see Maurice again.

"Back we go. There is another crop of rumors. Let's just pray we get out of here."

We retraced our steps. Elie went separately; and he reappeared with a pocketful of jewelry, antique pieces rarely seen now. "From a dealer I know. For cash in Zurich. He almost gave the stuff away. Those fellows are saying, sotto voce, that the Israelis are the medicine that Syria needs."

Shortly after we had left the garage, they stopped the car and inspected it minutely, under the hood and under the chassis. "He's a good man in that garage," said Maurice, "but he is living here and we'd rather make sure." There were no bombs. And from this point on, the spirits of the party began to soar. Christiane was ever so slightly hysterical, and her laughter ran ahead of everything. Maurice drove very fast to the frontier; it seemed that he had decided to crash through, but he stopped, and we waited for an hour or more, because the officials were searching and questioning. Christiane wore all the jewelry and flaunted it at the security officer, who in turn began to favor her. Then he snapped us past as though, if we didn't take the hint, he would lock us up for the sake of the girl.

Christiane was giggling afterward, and Maurice hugged her closer to him. He translated the cries from the radio: "O Arabs, prepare to die as martyrs, for martyrdom is the way to paradise. . . . We stand ready, O Nasser, you have shown the way. . . . Our heads are reaching up to the sky. . . . Aqaba is ours. We shall surely take it. . . . And let the Sixth Fleet go to hell! . . . We know the name of the beast that is against us: O America, we are coming to slay you! . . . Victory, victory, O Arab brothers, a new great age is dawning. . . . In this Holy War we shall spare no Jew—"

He switched it off. At first they had joked, Christiane as much as he, at the snarling yet lugubrious reader, making the most of his interminable text. The night was full of stars, and we were racing across the shadowy hills of Lebanon. After sight of Damascus (though not of any Russians) it was pathetic to hear this ranting broadcast. We were all indulging feelings of relief.

Then suddenly, the radio quiet, they sobered. It was, after all, a savage prospect.

Back at the farm we had another meal, then Elie took me down to Beirut. Maurice and his cousin looked pleasantly lost, exploring, out of that contentious day, some, perhaps an old, point of contact that was suddenly within their reach again.

3

THE DIARY OF
A DECISIVE WEEK
(June 5–11, 1967)

৵৹৽৹৵

MONDAY, JUNE 5

IT has been a shattering day.
Any war is shattering. If you have been in a war you are
paralyzed momentarily as the news of the next one comes
through. Life, which you feel through yourself, gives before
the mad, pounding beast. You sense, rightly, your share of the
blame.

I found myself saying, "I am terribly sorry. *Monsieur, je
suis bouleversé.*" It was the sense of loss that rooted me there,
as though love and hope had again been forfeited.

The concierge had pounced upon me, wheezing and cough-
ing, his transistor set stuck to his ear like a huge carbuncle.
His free hand threatened me with drama. Madame Suzette
was standing at her window in a military pose beside her
canaries. Suddenly I could hear that the whole street was
blaring with an identical madness. The concierge was crying,
"The Jews are bombing Cairo. *Les salauds, ils sont tombés
en démence.*" He too was shaken to his depths.

I decided to go to Sarkoubian's. It was too early for Raoul
or Leila. Sarkoubian has a house of his own in their main
quarter of Burj Hammoud, but you always find him at his
uncle's shop. That is where Leila sends for him. The uncle,
the one who bows excessively, is actually the patriarch among

them, and was at Diarbakir in 1915 when the Turks massacred the Armenians and the Tigris so ran with blood that four hundred miles away in Baghdad they had to stop using the water. Most of the family come from Adana and thrive on highly skilled crafts. There are 150,000 Armenians settled in Lebanon. S. himself is from Alexandretta by way of Port Said and Cairo. He has told me to read *The Forty Days of Musa Dagh* if I want to understand his story.

Their shop was full. How many of them? As Raoul says, they dissolve and appear like memories out of their own history. Are modern nations gross to them? The uncle was repairing a Sarabend carpet, the bench light on, indifferent to day. S. and his brother were reading papers, but the fresh news was coming from three radios. A son in the street was latched to one transistor set; another had a set with an ear attachment; and the main radio spoke from the bench. They were not missing the variations between Cairo, Damascus, and Beirut.

As usual, S. greeted me softly. He is a great admirer of the Queen of England. Coffee brought and a space cleared—incidentally so that I could see the prayer rug spread out the moment I appeared, which they probably guess is my second choice (my first choice they are hiding coyly)—S. gave a bit of the news. He did not give much. He barters everything. But I had passed cigarettes around. He gave out his news gingerly, as though it were wiser not to know. They are an infinitely resourceful and cunning people. They have had their measure of tribulation. They did not look alarmed at this moment. S. said that the Egyptians were claiming to have shot down twenty-three planes.

"Any news of a raid on Tel Aviv?"

They shook their heads. A younger boy, very brash, with a kind of jet black hair, recited: "From Cairo they say welcome to the Jihad, to the Holy War! We have been

waiting for twenty years for this moment. We have a
rendezvous in Tel Aviv. And from Baghdad they say, kill
the Jews! Radio Damascus is telling its listeners that the enemy
is already collapsing and that this year there will be summer
holidays for Arab people in Haifa and Jaffa and that also
the Arab oil workers must blow up the oil installations . . .
and"—he took a breath—"in Amman they repeat everything
that the King said yesterday. Here in Lebanon they say that
the army is already in the thick of the battle and that all
Lebanese stand united."

I thought of the Sheik's *coup de théâtre* last night. He had
only just got that one in.

But none of these radio cries sounded different from what
had filled the air for a week, although the whole context had
changed. The Arab hope, a prime reason for their threatening
propaganda, that America would restrain Israel had failed.
Arab policy lay in ruins. The Israelis were out destroying
aircraft—one presumed that they were not destroying cities—
as a logical first step in a war.

We had said there would be war. This didn't lessen the
horror of its actual impact.

There was something pitiful and extremely vexing about
these same Arab broadcasts. They had always lacked common
sense, for why bludgeon the world, why whine and scream,
why tout your affections like a silly coquette? They seemed
now not to belong to the realities of the morning in progress.

I asked again, "No strikes against Israel?"

They shook their heads. S. amended, "Syria says that her
planes are active. Egypt says that there is border fighting
and that over her territory she had now shot down forty-two
Israeli planes. She is calling for revenge. She says that Israel
has started a full-scale aggression."

They discussed this in Armenian.

Then the uncle said, "Do you know those words in Holy

Scripture? 'And God spoke unto Israel . . . fear not to go down into Egypt.'" He shook his head. "Perhaps already," he gestured obscurely. He bent to his carpet. "No revenge can be taken!"

This seemed, as it still seems this evening with as yet no hard news available, a most enormous supposition.

Yet with every hour it becomes more likely.

I still could not face Raoul or Leila. I couldn't say why; it might be the habit of not visiting them before tea time. I phoned canceling other appointments. I could feel that I was drawing back from Arabs. It was self-protective, perhaps, since I could not share any lust for Israeli blood. I deplore the colonialist stance of Zionism. I know that Arabs by the thousand have suffered inconsolable wrongs. Yet, since the creation of the Jewish State, I do not believe that Arab policies, heavy with hurt and bitterness and hate, mounting to a wild paeon of revenge, have done more than to lower the quality of their life. Economies stagger, psychopaths rage. The vocabulary of thought, already straitened by an uncritical view of their history, narrows further as they arm against Israel, which thus they themselves are shaping into a quite monstrous animal.

How different it could be! Through that most elusive of miracles—a change of heart, a change of understanding. Israel, from the start, has potentially been the local nucleus of western culture that the Arabs could absorb and learn through. (I take it for granted that they should absorb Israel, within this populous Arab region, but through osmosis, over a century, in the meantime correcting their own disabilities so that gradually the Israelis too would find their most natural extension within the wider Semitic society and leave the Zionist lifeline to wither.) Israel need not be indigestible. But for Arabs in blinkers the Kurds are indigestible, the Assyrians, the Copts, the Lebanese Maronites; in certain moods they reject in themselves their innermost need to absorb and to grow. They harden. They return to a desert vision uplifting them in a trance to Allah. They reject the world as it has to be lived in.

So once again the chance goes.

Downtown there was a small demonstration, with the usual flags and portraits of Nasser, heading toward the American Embassy. There might have been a thousand youths. They exulted in the war, and their fists toward heaven proclaimed their all-conquering mood. The police broke them up affably. As many as could crowded into bars for fruit juice and meaty *charwarma* sandwiches.

A woman at the side of the road was weeping.

The downtown scene was otherwise as usual.

I drove out to see John and Josey. Beeston of *The Daily Telegraph* had called. A tank battle was raging in Sinai. There was evidence of more Israeli air strikes. It all seemed to point one way.

Perhaps a man like Dayan inspires an image of invincibility. But we strongly felt that the Egyptians were finished. How they had always hated the desert with its wind-fashioned velvet morasses! *Fellahin.* Was it conceivable that they could feel at ease in Russian tanks? The Israelis would sweep through to the Canal before the UN could stop them. Slaughter again. And then what?

At some point the parties must negotiate.

The sheer desperation of this feud.

It was evening when I arrived at Leila's. I did not at once sense their feeling. Gaby and Marie-Rose and Lulu were cutting shapes from thick blue paper to drape around the standard lamps. Raoul, at the top of a stepladder, was spreading blue paint on the windows. Leila, in her chair, was heaving with mirth. They might have been preparing for Christmas.

Leila explained: "I am reading the instructions! Oh dear, if the elevator was not working, I could never get to the cellar in time!" She put into this simple predicament a whole day-long sense of agony. I could see now that she had been crying copiously. Had she moved out of that chair? Her mirth rose out of utter helplessness.

Not thinking, I cried, "Never mind, madame. It appears that the war is as good as over."

"What? What?" Her face went pale, expanding (it seemed) to twice its size. There was a scrape from the kitchen. The door was open. I later learned that it was Sarkoubian.

The girls must have thought that I was just being kind and paid no attention as they worked.

But Raoul . . . well, the incredible happened! He snapped at me from the top of the steps, "You are not, if you please, to spread that sort of rumor!"

"I'm sorry. But as you said last night—"

"But now it is war! Every Arab feels it. Why does the West support the Israelis? It is now we must know our friends from our enemies. We can strike, don't forget, through the Suez Canal! There is Arab oil. There are sterling balances! This is total war . . . on every front! Do you know that the Jordanians are attacking?"

"Yes."

"Well? We absorb the attack that may have been launched toward Gaza. We counterattack from the rear, from Jordan." He looked ill and fierce. He relented a shade, "You mustn't disparage everything that we Arabs do."

"I don't, Raoul. I'm really very sorry." I stared uncomfortably. It was he who disparaged. He was the most unpredictable person.

What a silence then! Snip, fold. The pant of Leila's distressed breathing.

She never dared rebuke her brother. She sighed. "*Inshâ'llâh,* we shall see it through. My dear, you are always safe with us. We will protect you." She took my hand. She smiled more easily, and the girls giggled.

But what in the world were they all believing?

I no longer dared ask.

When Raoul stepped down for a testy cigarette, I took his place and finished the painting. He lost interest and left the room.

Later I had a drink with S. the dealer. We purposely kept off the war. He uses words like "incredible people," especially for the local merchant princes who imagine that they have taste. He is still at Oxford, years ago.

Gordon Veitch came into the bar. He was battered but smiling, safe from Jerusalem. Government House had been an early target. The Old City, in fact, may well prove the key to the whole Jordanian sector.

A joint resolve: to go to the Kit Kat. The place was packed. A kind of wartime scene.

TUESDAY, JUNE 6

Beirut scorched by the fire of hatred. From early morning there was shouting on the radio and ugly shouts repeated in the street. I drove through town, and at the lights it was frightening being hemmed in by a pack of radios seeming to tear one limb from limb. The population was pressing to its radios as infants to the mothers' milk. There was a corner café on Boulevard Mazraa with a loudspeaker screaming outrage and ruffians with sticks scanning the cars as though deciding which to start on. Driving down a stretch of Avenue Shihab that was caught between two loudspeakers was like advancing through fire and brimstone. One sound in particular in Arabic matches the snarl of a leaping tiger. Other sounds are indescribable, as the tiger gets into your innards. You recoil from the hot breath of hatred. A tortured soul is torturing you.

It has continued all day. Even up in Brummana. Only this afternoon at Bkerke, at the Patriarch's Palace, could the peace of God be said to be encompassing all things.

I met Donato. It was not a good time for the niceties of social welfare. Maybe one should argue otherwise. He tried, certainly, with his buoyant account of how he had brought "understanding of the law," by helicopter, to Wadi Khaled, the outlaw-ridden tip of Lebanon. He has a buccaneer's personality himself—the most appropriate one for success in this country—and he triumphed where an army brigade would have failed. He went in alone, with medicines and school-books, putting an end to the reign of guns.

Leaving his office, I drove up to Brummana. One is used to shoeblacks and street hawkers being equipped with transis-tor sets—so that mingling with the cries of "O, sweet lemons!" and "O, try my beautiful cauliflowers!" comes the rancid propaganda—but here, on the gathering bends of the Mountain, were roadworkers sitting in the ditches, sitting on heaps of stones to be broken, also tuned to Radio Damascus. Their faces reflected lust for violence.

At the school there were scores of willing translators. By Government decree all schools are closed. This Quaker estab-lishment has a great many boarders from all parts of the Middle East, and, with lessons suspended, they were tuning in, these small fellows, in groups or singly, running or moping about the grounds, their transistor sets hugged instead of the books or balls they would usually have been carrying. How did they come to have these sets? Princes' sons, Ministers' sons, rich merchants' and farmers' sons, they presumably had any-thing they wanted.

"Sir," they accosted, "please explain why you and the Americans are bombing our airfields. . . . Sir, our King told us on Sunday that any nation that supports Israel has become our enemy for all time. Why have you become our enemy? You are fighting us, sir. Did your Queen give the order? . . . Yes, sir, we have heard it on the radio: President Nasser and King Hussein declare that American and English airplanes have actively assisted Israel. We heard it when we got up this morning. Why are you attacking my family? My father and my mother live in Jerusalem."

After lunch, it was still more persistent. Napalm had come into the attacks.

Seemingly, it had been the same in the village. It is a Christian village full of old scholars. But harsh things had been said that morning. The accusation was gaining credence. And why didn't the Queen deny it?

"But look, you know such a thing is impossible. I give you my word. It is a terrible lie."

"I am sorry, sir, I don't hate you personally, but from now on I must hate the British."

So it continued. I had to leave eventually. I felt sickened by this particular lie poisoning the younger generation. I felt sure it was a lie despite the unease caused by memories of 1956. It was just too unlikely a sequence. It was not as if Tel Aviv had been flattened—when, yes, the West would step in—so at some point we would step in. The explanation, on the contrary, must be that the Arabs were starting to excuse their defeat.

Already?

(I have just heard the late news from London and from Kol Israel. So it's this, it's clear.)

Well, back in Beirut, by three o'clock this afternoon I think that most of the Christian population were putting the same two and two together. The atmosphere had greatly changed, certainly in Ras Beirut. I had various small calls to make, and I left the car near the University. "This morning, actually, we were believing that you and the Americans had come in. Now we see you haven't. Nasser is losing." This thought seemingly had winged around the town, by telephone and service-taxi, by people dropping in on one another. The radio blare (in the more sophisticated quarters) was suddenly muted. People were relaxing. Unashamedly, their first reaction —among the Christians—was one of relief. Nasser had threatened their peace for too long—yes, speaking of it here in Lebanon—and now they could feel the nightmare lifting. "The *kabūs* is lifting!" Wonderful word.

They were beginning to tune to the BBC. One man said, "The Israelis claim. . . ."

Yet the dry cleaner with whom I left my jacket laboriously explained: "The Egyptians are winning. They are winning because they challenged the Israelis. They would not have challenged unless they had been sure in the first place that they would win!" This dry cleaner was a Sunni Muslim. When I suggested that he tune to the BBC, he said, "Monsieur, you have your radio, and I, I have mine!" He said it sweetly, accepting that men had different requirements.

Z., the most delightful of Lebanese gentlemen, took me out to Bkerke, to the Patriarch. Patriarch Meouchi, Cardinal of Rome, Patriarch of Antioch and All the East, could be approached as "*Éminence*" or "*Béatitude*," according to one's cast of reverence. Either way he was a formidable figure and a true heir to this formidable office. His residence was simple and unguarded, among the pine trees at a few hundred feet overlooking the Tripoli road. We awaited him in the reception chamber. He entered, his eyes flashing behind spectacles, a tall, huge frame of a man in red silks with his cardinal's hat. He was such a figure as Eisenstein chooses to depict the most powerful of boyars. He sat us beside him and leaned back, the big cross bumping on his stomach, as, with chuckling humor and mobile expression, he dived into a score of topics. For years he had been a parish priest in California, so he spoke English with vernacular ease.

"Is this our Lebanon?" he cried, with reference to the Nasser worship of the Beirut crowd, adding, "Many Muslims in a crisis such, dear doctors, as we see today come to me and beg . . . it is for you to say a word! I do not speak against men of faith. There are many fine Muslim doctors. I say to our country, only beware of paganism and of Communism. Are we to be like those who cannot earn their bread? These are times for slow and cautious judgments. And when we do not know, we look to Him"—he raised his hands in ritual devotion—"and we say, tell us what to do, help us, or take it on Your Own shoulders."

He twinkled. He was an extremely powerful man, the most imposing man of power in Lebanon, who behind the scenes had wires reaching, not just through his Maronite domain, but throughout Catholic Christendom.

Equally, he was a man of the soil, a mountain man, a great and simple shepherd. Therein lay his wide authority.

It is good to note that in 1958 he opposed the re-election of President Chamoun and worked for the acceptance of General Shihab. The Patriarchate, no doubt looking to the long-term interests of the Maronite community, is careful to speak first for Lebanon.

"Be assured that great changes are coming"—he was blandly winding up his dissertation—"yet in Lebanon evolution is slow." He twinkled. Make of that what you like!

In Beirut the evening news was somber. News from Jordan was coming in. There was Lebanese news, of food shortages, of profiteers and army recruitment, of attacks on the British and American Embassies, with cars burnt out and youths shot at. But the terrible news was coming from Jordan. Both

Jenin and Ramallah had fallen; a pincer attack was developing
on Nablus. The Israelis fought around the clock. For the
Arabs the whole horror was epitomized in the words of a
Jordanian soldier, relayed from a hospital in Amman: "We
did not see our adversary. . . . There was no man to fire
our guns at. . . . This liquid fire came from the sky." Napalm
was the horror topic.

How did such detailed news get over after the blanket
silence of yesterday? It must be that when armies are cracking,
nothing then can stop the news coalescing from rumor, a
phone call, an enemy broadcast, and the words of someone
who mysteriously has crossed the border. Beirut was suddenly
discussing estimates of Egyptian defeat. For how many hours
would the Arab Legion last? Was Syria to go scot-free?

What was going to be Russia's attitude?

America would be called to account now.

I note only what I heard myself in the St. Georges bar
and along our street and later while having dinner at Robert's.
In other parts of town quite different news—of Syrian attacks,
of Arab victories—was seemingly as widespread as ever. While
some people were anticipating Wednesday, others, probably
still the majority, were reveling in the hopes of the previous
Sunday. It is impossible to know how understanding divided,
except that the Christians were quickest off the mark and
were computing every decimal of advantage that might now
fall to their lot.

It was the first time that I had met Wadad. She was a
full-faced, energetic woman, devoted to the Arab cause in
Palestine. She ran a sumptuous household; they had three small
children. Robert looked relaxed with his children and almost
a trifle scared of her.

Over dinner she was cast down by the news. To recognize
something is not to accept it. She called, like a general, for
a Jordanian attack west out of Nablus toward the coast. She

shrugged, admitting that she didn't understand it. She berated the Americans. They would have to pay for assisting, if only in spirit, the Israelis. Well yes, she didn't believe they had been such fools as to send their planes over. But well, perhaps volunteers and coded messages. Time alone would tell all there.

She struck these attitudes, then let them fall away, because, under all, she was shocked and upset. Palestinian friends had been phoning since tea time, sobbing their fears for the fate of relatives. So many families had cousins in Jerusalem. Some had started a ritual mourning. It was a confused, horrible situation.

"It all began with the Balfour Declaration! How could your Government do that to us?"

"One can't always tell," said Robert more tolerantly, "how a decision will turn out."

As he spoke there was a vast explosion in the distance. (Heard later: the Shell refinery set on fire.)

I took a taxi home. At midnight I listened to the Israeli news from Jerusalem. They sounded jubilant.

WEDNESDAY, JUNE 7

I began the day at the American University. I was hoping to see Professor Chaamaya. The American staff were being evacuated. The library was shut. The campus was empty. It was an involved process to get in at all.

While waiting, I talked to some lecturers I knew. A spectrum of views—the most aggressive one was still relying on Egyptian rockets. Others were frankly deploring the harm done to their cause by Ahmad Shukairy. He should not have said that no Jews would be spared. Arabs had lived for centuries with Jews—Semitic brethren. There should be no division once the Zionist State had been smashed. It was mean, though, of General Murtagi to have put the PLA in the front line. And where were the Saudis, the Kuwaitis, the Iraqis, the Libyans, the Moroccans, the Somalis, the Algerians? Where were the hundred million Arabs?

The most thoughtful remark was, "But if the Russians are also agreeing to a cease fire, then our armies have been defeated. We don't want the Zionists to reach the Euphrates."

It was strange to see how yesterday's arguments could start up all over again, like domestic nagging, with new force.

Chaamaya was as discreetly dandyish as ever, discreetly keen to show a new purchase, a blue vase of Yildiz porcelain. He was gazing at it from wherever his talking and walking took him about his room, as though it summarized his aspirations. He grew stern when I asked his views on the war, as though, as a westerner, I had best keep quiet. Then quickly, throwing it out, he answered, "But of course, we shall have to start again . . . to fight again, after twenty years." Then he relapsed into a meditative silence and turned my attention to a literary matter.

Leaving, I ran into J.M., gleaming with the latest inside news. Our Ambassadors were going, so were most Americans, but the British community would be able to stay. Indeed, as I was able to tell him, the word coming from our Embassy was: "Be alert, be prepared, but do nothing!" He said, "All the same, be wary after dark. They don't know what has hit them yet. When the truth gets around, there'll be a hot reaction."

While he was speaking, Christiane appeared and asked to be let in through the gate. No students were being admitted unless one of the staff sponsored them. At all costs this great institution had to be kept free from trouble. "An American spy center, seize it!" one paper was telling the city. There had been student demonstrations on Monday. The academic year had been closed.

He nodded, and she was let through. She smiled wryly. She looked older, more her true age, than on the day with Maurice. In a querulous voice she said, "Thank you, Joe. Aren't you a part of this great exodus?"

"At gun point I might be."

He walked off, and talking—for today she seemed to be in a mood for talking—we went to the library. She was returning books. Then we stood in the sunshine. Later we had lunch together.

She was attacking America and praising Hamid for the new tone of his editorials. If the West, he was saying, would not recognize that Arab lands belonged to the Arabs, then Russian influence would increase here. Would this necessarily be a misfortune? Russia was a technological giant and temperamentally a part of the East. He eulogized the Russian temperament, so different from the opportunist Anglo-Saxons.

"But aren't Russians the greatest opportunists?"

Christiane, however, was to the left of Hamid. Marxist advisers, expropriation, a break with "the forces of world reaction": such was food and drink to her, along, of course, with what lay on the table. Like all the Hadiris she was a solid eater.

The current war, although she said with venom, "Yet another country taking to napalm," meant mainly for her the results that would flow from Nasser's "brilliant" collusion charge: that Americans by the thousands would be leaving the Middle East. (England she no longer thought important.) She couldn't help cheering when she saw them leave.

"But don't you have American friends?"

"Yes, I know. But America as such must be pushed back

on every front. Otherwise a point will be reached when none
of us can breathe any more. At that point there will be a
nuclear catastrophe. This is the gentler way of doing it."

She is some fanatic.

She also criticized Maurice. Is this because I saw them at
the farm? Doing so, she looked older still. Leila says that
he never will marry her, although he knows that her liking
for him has obstructed her other chances. That's how it is.
He will marry some kid. All the family pity Christiane and
are exasperated because, so wayward, she won't settle for a
conventional marriage.

She was saying, "He is far too pleased about the course
of the war! All that awful humbug on Sunday! He thinks
that the Muslims will be lost without Nasser and so lose
weight in Lebanon."

So the Sheik thinks this too? But I guardedly said, "Robert
sounded terribly depressed last night."

"Oh, Robert. He is a civil servant with plans, plans that
we have to fit into. When circumstances change, he is
temporarily blind. It is usually Hamid who rescues him."

Hamid again. The one she respects. The one who is not
just a counting machine.

She is such a beautiful, intelligent companion, with this
sour undercurrent of feeling. The family is absolutely right.

After lunch she had something else to do, but she inveigled
me into going along while, at the same time, pretending
reticence. We parked in the red-light quarter by the Burj.

"I know that the women here are trapped. And they mostly
hate it. It's the easy life and the shelter from the world before
which they are ashamed. You know, I can think of many
rich marriages which have landed girls in a similar plight.
They don't work the four-till-two routine, but they feel
soiled. They really go through it. Well, there's a girl here
that I'm helping with her children." Christiane was a shade

defiant, full of common sense but a shade excited. Wasn't she being exhibitionistic? She marched into one of the brothels —almost Japanese, with the patrona's name, like a score of others at this junction of streets, swinging in a neon sign above the door. The march up was bleaker, though: a tenement stairway with high, damp walls.

On the top floor we entered our establishment. There was no one around. There was a couch and chairs, a luridly abstract wallpaper, a radio, some small tables, and a large portrait of President Nasser. "Even here," I grumbled, "Big Brother never sleeps." "Oh, it's rather fine of them," she said. "Salma is a strong Arab Nationalist. I will ask her for you what she thinks of the war. Prostitutes also think, you know." She made this a proprietorial rebuke.

I must say, I admire her bearing.

Rather like A., long ago in Sweden.

She disappeared down a passage, then returned to fetch me. "Salma's up. You can come to her room." An over-furnished room with a large bed, big chairs, every kind of lampshade. Bric-a-brac on every shelf. A television set, a cupboard splitting with clothes. Bright new shoes in the middle of the floor, as though, like Chaamaya with his Yildiz porcelain, the owner had been gazing in rapture. Old shoes stuffed beneath the bed. The lamps were still on and the curtains drawn, but she now let in the sunlight for us. Salma was a plump, suspicious woman with what she might call her wild, little smile. "She is twenty-five," said Christiane, in now a very friendly and feminine manner. "She has lived here for the last ten years."

They chatted away like old companions. They laughed. It was a nice side to Christiane. "She says"—to pronounced nods from Salma—"that the Crusaders ruled for a century here, but that finally the Arabs got rid of them. The loss of a battle is not the war. She has a point, hasn't she?" Christiane purred, proud of her unlikely protégé. Meanwhile coffee, liqueur, and cream cakes were provided. There were whispers in the passage. "Each girl has her own room, but now the others would like to join us. Salma is not allowing them in. I'm sorry that you won't meet the patrona. I think Salma will soon buy her out."

"Why don't you help Salma to leave here?" I had seen the money that Christiane had given her, slipped over during their chat.

"I intend to, once the husband is chosen. It will help if first she becomes the patrona. She has two children who are farmed out now. Her family has never learned she is here."

"Did you meet her when you helped with the survey?"

"Yes. Tell you later."

Salma, suspicious, and with a rush of color to her fat, pale cheeks, had returned to preside over the refreshments.

Next she produced a photograph album, but at this point Christiane stiffened and with lavish excuses said we must leave.

Anyway, I think I have guessed. I'm pretty sure. There is a family likeness. For while they were chatting so closely together, I was studying the photograph standing among the litter on the dressing table. It was not exactly Maurice as a boy. No, I must amend, it was not quite Sami. Though the squinting smile places it nearer. Is this the epilogue to his youthful caprice? I saw him yesterday, off the St. Georges Hotel, water-skiing out from the boat club. Christiane is a saintly sister, yet there again there are mysterious factors.

Her excitement with Salma had overtones.

Outside she was closed and brisk, and she speedily went off elsewhere.

The Burj was seething with more political menace. "*Vous êtes français, monsieur?*" a man said nastily, as I was halted by the crowd and the service-taxis beginning to mill indiscriminately. "*Bien sûr. Français.*" An almost paralyzed shrug. Cowardly, but preferable to being lynched. I reached home safely.

Almost at once I was out again. Gordon V. was leaving for Rome. Officially Beirut airport was closed. Actually there was exit traffic. I drove him out. A sunset picture of scores upon scores of American families, rich but nonetheless refugees, with their children and luggage and their clean white teeth. The airport building was a shelter scene. Hussein, it was said, had given up; his fighting force had been cut to pieces.

I doubt he was ever allowed a free choice. Nasser has too much blood on his conscience.

The Israelis, it seems, have reached the Canal.

Midnight again, and quite fantastic. The Arab world is reeling with disaster; but a cool Israeli voice from Jerusalem, talking as though some mild epidemic was once again under control, announces that tomorrow the buses will be running on schedule throughout the city, that all schools will be open on Friday, that on Sunday a distinguished concert will be held. Boats are again scheduled for Tel Aviv. Bonds are on sale to finance repair work. Today—in this same laconic voice, it's a kind of terse chuckle—will be known nationally as Jerusalem Day.

I have just been listening to the weird ram's horn sounding from before the Wailing Wall.

One myth replacing another.

THURSDAY, JUNE 8

The local press is still batting away as though nothing significant had happened. "We refuse to accept the ceasefire. We say 'fight on!' to the Arab armies. . . . Till now the Israelis have not succeeded in winning a big enough military victory. . . . On to Tel Aviv, Arab brothers. Strike into the Israeli heartland. . . . We say to the West, we withhold our oil, we withhold the Canal; shall we bring you to your knees? We threaten you with a total boycott. Then let the Texan gangster talk!" More somberly one paper decides, "The war must go on even if the Arabs, even if the whole world, be annihilated."

Shukairy has shifted his ground to Damascus, whose radio is still convulsed by hatred. But from Cairo, in between short communiqués, the reading of the Koran has started.

Off rue Hamra a tourist agency is taking down its poster of Jerusalem, though outside, spread big on the pavement, another poster shows an Arab soldier, with the Palestinian flag fluttering in the background, bayoneting a hook-nosed Israeli.

The city seems very orderly and normal, noisy only in its usual ways. The dressmakers are crowded with women, the disc shops with girls in jeans. The service-taxis, which for the last two days have pretended not to notice fair-haired foreigners, are eagerly waving at us again. Because parking in the center of Beirut is so difficult, I usually don't take my car. I have hired it for exploring the country.

So I said to Raoul this morning, "Come on, let's take Leila for a picnic. And perhaps Lulu. Let's get out." I saw them, perhaps, as chaperons for Lulu. But I told him he looked too grey and weary from listening to the interminable radio.

Raoul has changed. He is now greedy for news. And although he foresaw this debacle, he is stunned. He won't talk much. It is almost as if he personally were shouldering the blame.

He said, "Sorry. Better count us out. But why not go to Bayt al-Din? You haven't seen it. You can't know now how long they will let you stay here!" He turned away, but Leila heard us, and she began telephoning, began shouting down the phone in the way she does, as though to span great distances. In the end this produced an enormous hamper and the company of Lulu and Marie-Rose and a student, Paul, to make up the party. And what a relief to get out of town!

Our instructions were to be back by curfew. But that did not start until 8 p.m.

We took the coast road south. This is considerably wilder than the road north to Tripoli. Sidon and Tyre (to give them ancient names) are little pockets of historical interest; where a fallen column or a vault or cloister or the tiny open sun-white harbors, like gravestones now, light up the past. They are growing again as market towns. But otherwise there are beaches, orchards, and olive groves climbing to crags that, backed no longer by towering mountains, suggest a gradual succession of hills.

We went south to Damour, then turned inland. A cloying smell of orange and grapefruit. We were heading primarily toward Druze country, these warrior-minded, occult sectarians. I find Kamel Jumblatt an unnerving personality. I can see him as a brilliant artist or scientist, with bohemian need to test his contemporaries with every kind of corrosive view; but he happens to be a leading politician, the titular head of a group of clans. An enfant terrible, didactically French, with the Druze spiritual exclusiveness. Because I'm a Quaker, he was nice to me personally, and rather shy the day we lunched together and swapped Yoga experiences. We have both done our stint in India. His castle of Moukhtara, more a manor house (only five miles from Bayt al-Din) is full of sketches and paintings of himself at all ages from favored childhood. The plaster on the ceilings is cracked and cobwebbed. In his mother's day it was still richly feudal, planted in this hard, martial landscape. A reconstruction of that time would make a lively book, and he, of course, is the man to write it.

His politics are similar to Christiane's. But the younger people are wary of him.

Lebanon is small. In forty minutes we were bowling up to Dayr al-Qamar, a strong post of the Maronite community, a center once of the silk trade that financed them out of their feudal allegiance. Earlier it was Fakh al-Din's capital, and for other Ma'n and Shihab princes until the building of the palace of Bayt al-Din. It is full of small princely mansions. We stretched our legs, took photographs, and discovered carvings and flights of steps, colonnades and marbled gazebos, one leading on to the next in the intervals of conversation. None of us was an ardent sightseer. Sightseeing has become devalued since it became a mass occupation. And these young girls knew more about Florence than they did of the treasures of their own country. We took it for granted that the main thing was to enjoy our talk and the lazy sunshine and let one's hand feel the old stone and one's eye travel on down the valley.

The same at Bayt al-Din, six minutes away. Magnificent in scale against the hill and the village; and cool with slender pillars and fountains and inner courts and outer gardens. Perhaps why we lingered and talked and gazed, while the hardened guide was anxious to proceed, was the wish to be living in such a place, with the leisure to absorb its life. Lamartine, Lady Hester Stanhope, Warburton, and other visitors have had that leisure, and also the privilege of being the guests of the Emir Bashir. Today, in the summer, Charles Helou is in residence. All over the world these choice buildings are becoming museums or secretariats.

Where to have the picnic? It was midday and hot. But Marie-Rose (Maurice's sister) had thought it out, and we climbed to Ain Zhalta, at 3500 feet, then a little way on to an orchard nook beautifully pleasured by waterfalls; and there was an acre belonging to the father of one of her maternal aunt's maids. They found it more natural to picnic on the ground of someone they knew than otherwise. They invited the old peasant couple to join us, but these, on the contrary, brought fruit and cheese and later coffee, but they would not sit down.

Lulu at last began to cheer up.

She is the sweetest among Les Jeunes Filles, but she has mother trouble. A year ago, fed up with playing the young lady in the endless round of tea parties and cocktail parties, she begged to be an artist. So an artist she became. But then Mama (or so she puts it) incited her friends to look in as usual, no longer for cakes, but to praise her talent and to beg to see the latest canvas or latest slight sketch. So much talk of genius followed, which was even more soporific than their talk about husbands, that she gave it up. She had a spell in the States.

She came back this spring to start a "crazy boutique." She had really thought of starting it now, in Bhamdoun, for the summer season. This week Mama said no, not now. Oh, of course, the war. . . .

She was still principally blaming her mother.

Lebanon wasn't involved in the war!

Les Jeunes Filles seem to shun the war except when Aunty Leila is nervous or some choice gossip drops from their parents.

Apropos of this, Marie-Rose, over lunch in that cool idyllic picnic place, with the hills shimmering and slipping from the eye and the valleys turned to pools of mist—against this background she let fall that Maurice had heard that large funds had been withdrawn from a certain bank by a certain party, and that that indicated serious trouble. Revolts, riots; all required cash. The family were coming to the hills on Friday to be out of Beirut during the weekend, except—guess who?—cousin Farid. He was eagerly sharpening his teeth.

She dropped this nugget; and she also told the joke about the Lebanese pilot who had strayed over Israel. Then she returned to the things that interested her.

We passed most pleasant hours in the orchard and scrambled

up to the rocks above. Then, reluctantly, back to the city.

Leila was delighted. Raoul scowled. He told the girls that starting tomorrow they must help with the Red Cross work for Jordan, packing clothes for the refugees. He was absolutely right, and they saw it too. Yet, was it necessary for him to be so testy?

Spent the evening in my apartment. Elated, rather. Made an omelette, made telephone calls, and listened to the news from London. This, at last, has come up to date. A group discussion about the future of Israel, to be composed more equally of Arabs and Jews, so becoming just another Middle East state. Desirable, I think, and the shock of war always produces desirable ideas. Then these ideas fade away. Nasser has accepted the ceasefire. It would seem that his army has been crucified. What about the thoughts, today, of the governments, including our own, that have poured arms into the region? Will they promptly pour them in again?

Their computers, the pets, will advise them to do so.

I am curious about the last thoughts of a computer as our civilization goes up in fire.

Begin making notes: the Hadiri family, their relationship with Muslims, the additional tensions within this country arising from the war. Why not set it out in a book? I can't claim to remember every conversation, but I roughly do; these days are so alive. Too frank and intimate? Very hard to be that in an age of all-revealing television.

Be thankful one can still make a case for writing.

FRIDAY, JUNE 9

The concierge stops me again. I haven't spoken to him since Monday. "Monsieur, I am pleased that Nasser is not strengthened, but, speaking as an Arab, I feel humiliated." He stands there, bereft of pride, seeming to seek our old relationship. He has been telling people that I am a British spy and that if it hadn't been for Sheik Nassib's protection he would have taken his razor to me. Sarkoubian has tipped me off.

I give him five Lebanese pounds. I praise his sons and speak of my own. We confer as parents, considering life.

"Monsieur," he continues, "is it true what they say, that all Arabs will be banned from Europe?"

"Not one," I assure him. "We respect the Arabs. We have also been trying, out of respect for all men, to understand the Israeli position."

"Ah, monsieur"—he wheezes hoarsely—"put such a hopeless attempt behind you. Perhaps the Arab is not fit enough yet, physically speaking, for this kind of war. But in the next generation, I tell my sons, they can go out and obtain justice."

He goes back unhappily to his radio. Actually he has spent his life in this quarter, arguing events up and down the street. The mood of resignation does not suit him.

Next stop, the *dhobi* man, for the suit he had promised by yesterday evening. Seeing me approach, he starts on it now. To press the trousers, leg by leg, he throws a dirty cloth over, wets it with a sponge, then presses hard with his steamroller of a charcoal iron. He completes this in a flash, and signals his assistant, who runs off, to return with beer. Cigarettes and a pause for beer. He shows me an Arabic magazine with the photograph of a near-nude girl. "Nice?" His voice and the honeyed movement of his hand demonstrate how he would caress her. He likes, he tells me, to go swimming with girls. He conjures up Arabian delights. Then he is back at work, very swiftly again, smacking his iron down on the jacket and dealing with the joint of sleeve and shoulder by holding it up to fit a cloth block under, then ironing it held up there in the air. The result is perfect. He won't take payment. "The maid will see to it next time she passes."

I could have spent all morning in the street. Many of the

street's inhabitants do, all the year, all their lives, either with the single pilgrimage to Mecca or with the equivalent journey to Jerusalem to give them the authority of distant places. They make of the street itself a journey, a magic carpet through space and time, with an ever-changing variety of moods, each of which they live intensely. Even Leila in her panoramic room feels these moods, is fed them by Hoda, who is dispatched on errands several times a day. One goes from a backgammon game in the café to have coffee with Leila on the seventh floor and is surprised to find her echoing the amusement of the latest street-level story. And through the street she reflects the city. She never needs to move at all.

Called on Maurice Shihab, the Director General of Antiquities, in his offices behind the National Museum. The emir Maurice has princely charm, which is to say he's efficiently outspoken and learned and in everything conscious of the role played in the history of Lebanon by his family. When he says of Maronite patriarchs that "in the days of the emirs, they kissed the emir's hand," and of Sunni leaders that they block their own progress with their sense of superiority, and of the Druzes that they are inward-looking, he is very properly, like his ancestor Bashir, subordinating all to princely order. He seems to like remembering that Bashir was baptized Christian, married as a Muslim, and could always convince the Druzes he was Druze. As he put it, "today I have cousins of each faith. We live amicably, as cousins should." Lebanon's problems thus solved in his mind, he turns his attention to her earliest history and discourses on Phoenician figurines, explaining the sequence of form and garb.

So passed an enchanting morning, detached from all else, a continuation of yesterday's idyll in the countryside.

Too good to last. The town was again stirring. Nasser's portrait might be disappearing, and the radios largely restricting themselves to patriotic songs, but the war was still continuing, in Syria now, and this was producing fresh insecurity and more bad nerves. Syria in turn was being battered. Many here distrusted the Syrians and abominated their present regime. Still, Syria was next door to Lebanon. I saw Ghassan Tueni, the proprietor of *Al Nahar*, and he said bluntly, "The Zionists intend, now or later, to take South Lebanon. They covet all the sources of water. That is what they are going for in Syria. You hear only about the Syrian Heights and the shelling of the Tel Katzir kibbutz, but read of what already they were claiming—it was for Palestine then—in 1919, and you know that they are after the source of the Baniyas and for a hold upon the Yarmuk river. Next stage, they will claim the Litani."

He is a clever and humane newspaper owner. During an interview he comes and goes to give snatches of thought to the next room where a journalist or editor is working, and he returns to give extra pungency to the thought he is concurrently developing with you. His paper, in the delphic manner of today, tests out difficult opinions. He is known, in this city of bombs and razors, for extreme loyalty to editorial staff.

He was saying, "Arab states must align their policies even to keep a minimum security. Lebanon cannot vary that fact. She is vulnerable. That's what we see now. And toward the West, who created Israel and continues to render her existence possible, we can only say that the Arabs will never accept the creation of the Zionist State. Ah, a Palestine with both Jews and Arabs—produce that, and we'll talk again! But as things are, we oppose the West; we reject her along with her protégé Israel; and we shall continue the fight with diplomatic weapons."

I asked him why in his Wednesday's edition he had given front-page headlines to "collusion" and a back-page insert to the Western "denial." He must have known the charge was a lie.

He shrugged. He had really given me his answer. "Arab policy is consolidating around Nasser's charge of collusion. Naturally, therefore, it is front-page news."

On leaving his office, I had a drink with Maurice. This curfew is ruining evening invitations. One has to crowd things into the day. He warned me to be wary this evening. Nasser's announcement, promised for seven, whatever it tried to explain away (they were saying, a billion dollars of armaments, the shreds of an army, man by man, straying waterless across the desert), would be dynamite for the Muslim masses. They still barely knew what had hit them.

He was in a cautious mood. He keeps ahead of events. Far from crowing over the fact that the "Muslim position" would be weakened in Lebanon (as the average Maronite does more and more), he had repositioned himself with sagacity. He was talking of the chance of a better understanding.

His one light touch: Syrian political prisoners, released from Damascus jails today to be able to fight for their country, had quickly scuttled over into Lebanon.

Now we have it! Nasser has resigned. His television appearance, haggard and hesitant, showed the leader stripped of grace: a downcast image that gave the cue for extraordinary scenes of despair. Professional mourners could not have done better. A woman extended her arms in supplication, wailing "O Nasser" and clawing at her hair, her throat, and down her dress to her breasts. A youth threw himself brutally to the ground. From the Burj, lurid with the red of sunset and a half-response to the blackout rules, up toward the Muslim quarters, little groups like tribal dancers were swaying and acting out their grief.

It was not a concerted mass demonstration, but a thousand little enactments of tragedy, of stunned response to the hand of fate. There was a deep-throated, monotonous chanting of "Nasser, Nasser," with yearning in it. But there were some in

cars whose tone was more insistent—"Nasser, Nasser!"—and
they were quickening the pace, as with the faithful in a foot-
ball crowd. Their cry sounded more professional, and it was
they who led the few hundred followers who finally assem-
bled, still shouting and beseeching, before the residence of
the Eyptian Ambassador.

His Excellency Abdel Hamid Ghaleb (usually known as the
High Commissioner) responded with a speech from a crowded
balcony. Raoul had declined to come along, and I myself was
not chancing conversations, so I missed the import of that
speech. But the floodlights showed up passionate faces, and
the burst of shouts and handclapping and motor hooting both
pleaded and insisted and finally broke up (with an extension
of the curfew—but even after that the town was running,
running and roaming, and leaping in the shadows, with dis-
oriented human figures) on a note of frantic determination.
Nasser was the pivot of all that feeling. The loss of their god-
king was absorbing all the other emotions of the week—as his
resignation speech had uncannily invited.

For thousands of fervent Muslim Arabs, those hours looked
to be a traumatic passage, never in their lives to be forgotten.
Suicidally, perhaps, they would still offer themselves if only
their god-king might be restored to them.

SATURDAY, JUNE 10

An ugly day. By eight there were some youths already on the
streets, shouting and hammering on shop shutters. They looked
as though they had been up all night. Our street bully was
among them. They went to and fro, clustering, returning at
a quickened pace, then they vanished again. Other loud cries
came from the neighborhood; and from the nearby main

traffic throughway, instead of the usual morning hum, came the spasmodic blaring of motor horns. The radio had announced a general strike, ostensibly in support of Nasser. But it had the merit of keeping people at home. Many faces were peering from balconies, then retreating within. There was a changed pulse coming off the street, a rapid flickering of agitation, intermittent, incredibly sinister.

There would come the beginnings of the Nasser cry, a sort of battle chant, then ragged silence. Then, seconds later, the ruffians were there, menacing as yet, not doing anything.

But when the café opened its doors, they yelled and smashed all its windows, grouping upon the scene in seconds. It was about then that they slashed the tires of three large cars, each of which belonged to a Christian.

Then, inexplicably, they disappeared.

The way seemed clear. The concierge was sitting in his little room listening to the radio. "I have no sympathy for the Syrians," he told me. "They now appeal: 'Come to our aid.' But did they go to the aid of Hussein? Hussein is the best man among the Arabs. He has courage, monsieur. When he said we will fight to the last breath until we face God, I wept. Don't go out, monsieur. There are dirty men about. They are being paid to kill the Christians. Let them go to their mosques and mourn Arab dead."

I was touched that he no longer saw me as an enemy.

But then, as a Christian, he too was on guard.

Curiosity and the peculiar idea that a general air of harmlessness will see one through most situations (I am glad that it wasn't put to the test) propelled me out into the car. I went downtown and parked near the suqs. On the way, at the entrance to the Jewish quarter, two cars had been burned out. There was an array of broken windowpanes. There were troops on guard, the first troops I saw other than those outside the Embassies.

It was now evident where the ruffians had gone. The Burj seethed with demonstrators. It was a rallying ground, for more were arriving, and every man seemed to carry a stick. A loudspeaker was giving directions, and posters were being stuck up everywhere, portrait upon portrait upon portrait of Nasser until the entire square seemed alive with Nassers, the core of whatever action was to follow. Flags, banners, posters were waving. Some purposeful men were addressing the assembly, which began to move away up the hill.

"Where are they going?" I asked an obvious effendi.

"To the Egyptian Embassy. To the American Embassy." He grinned. The objectives would be totally different.

I decided to report on this to Raoul. But Raoul too had gone out investigating, and Leila was half-crazy with worry. He was supposed to have gone to an apartment on rue Hamra, but so far he had not turned up there. We waited ten to fifteen minutes, then I said that I would go and find him. He might be sitting in The Horseshoe Bar. That kind of place would be open.

"Are you mad?" she exclaimed, her eyes popping. But I said that it would be on my way to Raouche, where I was expected for lunch anyway.

"You are coming here for dinner," she said, as though to insure my safety meanwhile.

It was not so easy to get out this time. Some flickering figures were back in the street. They had just smashed the shoemaker's window. They were real footpads, the weevils of trouble, and they vanished only to circle back before one had a chance of getting clear. Then a sustained blaring on the throughway attracted them, and the crash of some major destruction; and once in the car I took the other direction, down to the sea, and along the Corniche.

No better luck here. Security police had cordoned off the road. I produced the bit of paper Robert had given me, but it didn't work. The officer told me that there was a hostile crowd near the British Embassy. No point in going in that direction. Nothing for it but back to the Burj.

It seemed quite safe so long as one was moving. There were a fair number of motorists about, couples, even families with children, beginning, as we swung past the suqs where the signs and sounds of destruction mounted, to take the universal sightseer's interest. It's odd, but a motorist feels protected (so long as he is in a stream of motorists) from turmoil among mere pedestrians. We are the tanks; they, the infantry. Fortunately, again, this wasn't put to the test.

Approaching Hamra, we really ran into it. Here, as everyone is now explaining, was the methodically organized trouble: the vehicles set upon fixed circuits, so many to each round of streets, so many trucks, so many men, so much money to be paid out afterward, not excluding the cut that goes to the big bosses behind the scenes. Civil disturbance, like a revolution, pays some pockets well in the Middle East.

However, what we actually ran into, unsuspecting, at that juncture, was a riotous cavalcade of trucks railroading down rue Hamra, rue Naccache, Avenue Bliss, Sadat, Jeanne d'Arc, Abdel Aziz, and all the other one-way thoroughfares of this conspicuously westernized quarter; railroading through the ever thinning traffic that rapidly fanned out of the way; and in these trucks were gangs of men hurling stones at neon signs and at windows, and belaboring all they could reach with their sticks. As I went past The Horseshoe (its large picture windows had been smashed to smithereens; it was dark, deserted, as was every café down the street), there came a drumming of blows on the roof of the car. Sick with fury, I cheered up when I saw it was happening to the other cars.

After the trucks came passenger vehicles crammed with shouting, gesticulating youths who were also waving portraits of Nasser. One could see that they had been busy early, for where yesterday afternoon hardly a portrait of Nasser had survived, now the streets were covered with posters. Everywhere Nasser smiled on the scene. It was his scene, a timely reminder that the *kabūs* had not been lifted.

The visible damage was tens of thousands of dollars. A whole quarter was being taught a lesson. Uglier, perhaps, were one or two scenes where cars were being flagged down by youths, who then scrolled "Nasser, Nasser," in Arabic, with white paint on the windows. People who objected were being threatened. One man was being hit. It suddenly looked as hard to avoid this as to cross the Line without a dip from Neptune. The trucks relentlessly were coursing around, with the hail of stones and the whacks from the sticks. The crazy youths were blowing their horns in prolonged bursts as they stormed after (nobody taking any notice of lights); and above there was a helicopter watching. There was no point in staying. Another drumming on the roof, and the certainty that a painting squad had at last noticed my unpainted condition sent me spinning down a one-way street the wrong way (they didn't break that rule), and so over the hill to Raouche. Guilty about Raoul, I phoned his friend. It was okay. Raoul was there.

Far away in England it was my younger son's birthday, so with John and Josey I celebrated here. Thank goodness there were a few other things to talk about. And, as they said, to anyone who had been in Cairo during the riots of 1951, today was almost a non-starter.

Still, not quite.

D.B. rushed in. He had actually been chased by a mob and had hidden in a cupboard in a strange building. There had been shooting in town. The Kataeb was involved. Maronite leaders had gone to the President and declared that if the destruction did not stop (it had wholly been directed against Christian property), they could not answer for what their followers might do to the Muslim quarters. Ignition Point. The clear possibility of another 1958. Fortunately, Bustani, the acting Commander-in-Chief, had understood his responsibilities. An unknown quantity (with Shihab usually there), he had this week given signs of his character (he had had to deal with demands that Lebanon should suicidally launch an attack); and he had just ordered an emergency curfew. Troops were in the streets. The gangs, the youths, had faded back into the earth.

A cooling off. Once again the military were having to calm the politicians.

But still, before this, more openly than usual, the politicians had shown their hands.

The curfew lifted at five o'clock for a couple of hours. The streets a travail of broken glass. Scrunch go the tires. A mad schoolboy's landscape. Sightseers out by the thousands. The military definitely top dogs now. Tanks taking up position.

This evening, the dinner party at Leila's. The other guests were from the second floor, Mr. and Mrs. Saam and their daughters. Saam had his tires slashed this morning and he was vengeful and calling for impossible reprisals. He is a Christian who hates the Muslims' guts. He saw today's events as a sneak raid, with most of the army down on the frontier. "We should proclaim Lebanon to be Christian and neutral. Haven't we thousands of relatives in America? How shameful to be linked with Abdel Nasser!" He could not stop reviling Nasser, going on about it uncontrollably. Jails, torture, assassination—Nazi techniques—the sell-out to Russia. The whole catalog flowed off his tongue. Raoul frowned at the gushing emotion but said very little to start with.

Leila was bewailing the fate of Jerusalem, fallen into the hands of the Jews. What would happen to the Holy Places? Muslims at least had been respectful. She didn't seem to grasp that the fighting was over, that her immediate torrent of fears could settle, and, contrary to all she had always maintained, she was saying that at least Nasser was a moderate, that changes must not happen too quickly. To Saam she said, "But the *fellahin* were wickedly exploited before Nasser! Perhaps Syria is the cause of the trouble." She told us that yesterday evening at Harissa the great statue of Our Lady of Lebanon had shone, in the surrounding darkness, with a halo of divine light. Our Lady had turned to either side to make sure all was well with Lebanon. Many women had seen the miracle. Leila was in a bewildered mood.

The two girls looked fat and hapless. Beirut, apart from its slim coquettes and its ravishingly modest harem beauties, has its share of ox-like females. These two, with no better sense than to sit on either side of a sideboard so that they made a foursome with the two heavy jars standing on that piece of furniture, sat softly sweating and listening and moving their thighs with a nylon swish, opening and closing these huge protuberances as though in never-ending yawns. I'm not sure whether they spoke all evening.

Their mother was trying to soften Raoul.

Now, anyone who knows Raoul at all knows when he's in a mood to leave him alone. Don't try to make things better. If you have to talk, outdo his irony. Be more mordant than he is.

She, alas, was being frivolously sugary.

In any case Raoul had made it clear that, apart from other aspects of the war, he was stricken by the plight of the refugees. That vein of misery opened deeper. He just didn't want to talk to the Saams.

But they made him talk. And Saam, with a joke that he had culled from an Israeli broadcast, about Dayan choosing Russian arms for the Arabs, suddenly set Raoul blazing. Not a fiery blaze, but the black kind. Raoul began defending Nasser. Nasser had vision. Nasser was an Arab. For Nasser to have been cast off now would have been to leave them at the feet of the West. It was the moment actually to regroup about Nasser (perhaps the first moment that all Arabs could say this) and not to look to America or Russia or China, or to anyone else, for anything. The Arab must draw into himself, be purged, be proud to stand alone. To hell with the West and its modern technology (and Raoul for the moment really felt this). If necessary, better to live in the desert.

Leila nodded, understanding her brother.

Saam said, "You are not being serious!"

Raoul replied, "I would rather die, I would choose death for all the Arabs, than accept what the West has in store for us. Monsieur Saam, I can see it clearly. Let us throw away our arms. They are no use to us. Let us walk unarmed across the frontiers of Israel, a hundred million Arabs, till they tire of killing us. Let us move on further, take ship to Europe. Let us walk through Europe, let us walk through America, till the last Arab falls dead! Let us die in the flesh to live in the spirit. If we live on the terms you suggest, monsieur, we are already dead, worse than dead."

Raoul blazed with nihilistic vision, at the core of which was something precious.

For me, not an Arab, he was unapproachable.

He was savagely, in the debacle which he certainly felt, trying to find out who he was now.

Possibly some phase in Beirut had finished for him.

SUNDAY, JUNE 11

First to the Phoenicia to send a cable. The curfew is on till 9 a.m. But the sentry I come across is staring at the sea and crooning to himself. The hotel halls, empty to the eye, echo still with American voices, filling in a day before flying to

Jerusalem. What future now for the tourist trade? They could equally well fly on via Cyprus. It would be a pity if they flew straight to Israel and so missed the Lebanese mountains. Baalbek, the Cedars, Bayt al-Din, all are okay. These are the sights to set in the ledger. But the real physical well-being comes from uncharted hours spent in the hills. Americans, don't let your travel agent talk you out of that one.

But Lebanon needs a different tourist policy, less snobbish and less clichéd. It could learn from the practice in Greece, Spain, or any East European country. It could profit by being less noticeably keen on extracting every shekel.

At five to nine I was in the car, in a shoal of cars in Fuad Shihab, at the junction of the Damascus road. We had all patently broken the curfew, but the officer, counting down with his watch, was only concerned with his junction. After two minutes the horns started blaring. We're all Lebanese, old chap! No luck. Bilious, he shouted to his troops to face us with their rifles. The hooting stopped, but expressive arms gestured, telling where to put it. He made an example of the foremost car, placing the driver under arrest. Then, with thirty seconds to go he flicked us away with a gesture that said, "Why am I pained by flies and microbes?" He had to jump as we accelerated.

Up in Brummana, up in the cool, the scene had totally changed since Tuesday. Most of the boys had gone home; others were awaiting charter aircraft; yet others were still without news of parents, their ears filled with the horror reports crowding out of Jordan. Were their fathers the victims of napalm, were their mothers at the Allenby Bridge, salvaging a few heirlooms in a pram for the sake of living in Arab freedom? The high challenging note had been muted into one of fretful bewilderment.

During Friends Meeting we sat mostly in silence. Miss Faridi, the dear old lady who has a drawer full of Lawrence's letters, spoke of the burden of the Arab world. She reflected, I think, much of its feeling when she said that that burden must be placed with God, that humans could not fathom His ways, and that there was nothing more they could do. Bewilderment and heart-searching and return to the feet of the Primal Mystery. On Friday the King of Morocco had cried that Arabs had sinned, that defeat was their punishment. And in Beirut the Mufti had reminded his listeners of the angels who had assisted Muhammad, that believers should hope for such help again. A turning inward. A humbling of self. A yearning for the pristine purity of the desert.

We sat in the sunshine after Meeting, some of us Arabs and some of us British, tender in spirit, as Friends are. I have known this tenderness in every continent. It has the power to move mountains. It gets lost often in the failures of language, as we, bending to the speed of the century, are continuously changed, some faster than others, yet cannot express what is happening. We have the words for a decade ago. We miss one another in the bogs of syntax. Silence reunites, however.

We had a good Quaker lunch, then went for a walk. It was hot by now, and the cicadas were chirping. The villagers were friendly again, thinking more of their mountain summer. Scores of families had also moved up here, early, out of the tensions of the city. The hotels had opened. The cafés were packed. The play of holiday shopping had started. The road was a press of cars and pedestrians.

Below, stretching to the sea, was mist.

This also was a form of withdrawal: the hope that by autumn things would be better.

The grocer said, selling cigarettes, that yes, if the Israelis seized this opportunity to make amends for 1948, if in victory they could be magnanimous, especially with regard to the refugees, there would be a settlement. Arabs were gentlemen.

The question was, were the Jews gentlemen? Were the Americans or the Russians gentlemen? The British—he sucked his teeth sadly—we hadn't cut such a good figure. We had an old name, but not the men to go with it. With each successive crisis here, our stature was seen to be diminished. He was going to repair his terraces: make sure he grew more of his food. Well, perhaps by autumn it would be better. . . .

It was summer now. Summer in the village.

Back in Beirut I had time, before the curfew, to run round for tea with the Zoghals. This was the ten-day-old invitation, to visit their summer villa at Aley. Najla had said that I still should come, but to the town house. They were occupied there.

There were a number of people, indoors and in the garden. What might have been a leisured company against that setting, as on a Persian frieze, was actually, overall, distraught, broken into groups that by the passion of their talk seemed to be trying to reverse events. The telephone was constantly ringing. Najla, her doe-like beauty crumpled by the sufferings that hourly accumulated, was trying to comfort a sobbing guest. Arab grief knows no bounds, is murderous and suicidal together, and cannot be borne by a Western observer. I tried to leave, but she told me to stay until I had seen Hamid. I couldn't find him, but I found Ali—or this time he found me: an intruder in their midst he seemed to define me, although his approach was icily polite.

He was not (have I met an Arab who is?) interested in an adversary's view. He cut and thrust with what he had to say— more evidence of western collusion: the Wheelus Air Force Base had assisted Israel—the bankers here were a fifth column, and should be publicly tried and, he would hope, shot, along with corrupt Egyptian generals—the war had turned the Arabs to the Left: the next stage, of unified planning and marshaling of the Arab masses, would principally lie with Boumedienne.

The Algerian leader, together with the Syrians and the Chinese and certain of the Russians, was now the man to organize victory.

"But don't you want to negotiate peace? Surely your backers, the Russians, do?"

"I rejoice," he answered, "in the Israeli pilot hacked to pieces by Egyptian peasants. I glory in the pilot hacked to pieces in Damascus. I am joining Al Fatah to take the war into Israel, to kill whoever falls in our path."

"You know, that's an inhuman thing to say."

"Don't speak to me of what is inhuman!"

We were saved from a quarrel by Hamid's appearance. He very sharply waved Ali off.

"I am sorry," he said, "but his generation feels—well, we all feel this disaster. Defeated in six days! It's incredible. It will be a year before the damage is counted and all the heads that must roll will be known." He seemed, if I may say it, impressed despite himself. His large, warm, thoughtful personality was brooding with a new appraisal of events. He cast a compassionate eye on the sufferers, but his own work lay elsewhere. "Let's talk," he said. "The Western press has shocked us with its support for Israel. Our propaganda has been misguided. We are over-inclined to scold America as though we, not they, were the major power. I think we shall have to be more realistic."

"A total boycott wouldn't work?"

He dismissed it. "Not here. But Lebanon is small, though our voice will become more important now. We shall fairly easily ride this setback and perhaps point the way to our Arab neighbors. The truth is that we, the Arabs, have to start from scratch again and to change course.

"Yes, yes," he went on, "I know that I have been calling publicly for assistance from Russia. I don't need to retract that view. The change comes in the form of assistance. Dear friend, what we must turn our mind to, forgetting about arms and war, is technological education, the development of each Arab economy and of each of these in unity with the others. We have a chance to learn from our defeat. There is no point in our challenging Israel, nor, let me add, in talking to her, until we are as advanced as she. That will take us half a century, and by then the problem may not exist. This is the only option open. I place no faith in the UN, no faith in Big Power promises. I deplore my son Ali's views. I say we must take our coats off, bend to the task. We should take help, scientifically, from America, from Russia, from Britain and France. In fact, we must grow up finally!"

I told him about Raoul's outburst.

"Ah, he's a poet. I am a journalist. You will see the change in my paper from tomorrow. Let the West, let America in particular, see that the Arabs can learn in time. No more hard words from me, sir."

It struck me, during this week of warfare, that Raoul and Hamid had almost changed places.

Arab kaleidoscope.

Arab humanity.

4

THE
MOUNTAIN
VIEW

WHERE had yesterday's heat gone? We were up before dawn and crossing the village, and a night breeze from over the mountains gave a chilly start to the walk.

We had eaten a good breakfast. After a coffee and the wafer bread and olives and cheese, and then a dish of yogurt and figs, I had followed Raoul in eating some *kishr* warmed up with the revolting smell that *qawwrama*, the mutton fat, always gave (a smell extending with Arab culture from the Atlantic to the borders of India, where it changes into that of *ghee*). Apart from what he was taking in his knapsack, it might be our last food till evening. Usually the peasants had it cold at this hour, but the old woman wanted to please us. She had been out in the dark in the garden plot choosing pears for us to take. She had been out to the adjacent flat-roofed building (where in daytime she sorted beans and eggplant and tomatoes for simmering and bottling as paste), she had been for water, she was attending to the frying. One only heard her step suddenly, for she moved and worked with great stealth. She clucked with pleasure at doing something for us, before her son the householder rose and threw his arrogant, gloomy shadow over the narrow world of the women. He also rose before dawn, but today we were an hour ahead of him.

We walked swiftly through the sleeping village. There was a smell of fruit and herbs in the air, blending with the fresh smell of one's linen, washed with laurel in the mountain water. This spiced freshness was exhilarating. It was part of the goodness the peasants knew, with their land and kin securely about them, before the hard hours of the day. There was no one at the fountain, no one at the church. The elder still slept in his house, the metal shutters of his store closed. There were shadows everywhere, and dogs stirring, and moonlight glancing off car hoods. Hoda's fiancé was still asleep, his old Mercedes beside the house. There were a large Plymouth and a Dodge next to it, both belonging to summer visitors. He had been working late last night on the cars, after his last run up from the city.

Leaving the village, we came to Raoul's house: what was at last signed and witnessed, his buildings and his two *dunums* of land. The men had been working for a month upon it, and it was almost ready for occupation. In fact, some nights he had slept there, in the heat beneath his apple trees, in an excess of his new wave of feeling. The war disaster of a month ago had burned through the old cynical Raoul, plunging his outer personality into prolonged bouts of silence, which I for one had misinterpreted until I had seen the new verse he was writing, which showed up the inner changes, showed that, discarding futility and bitterness, he was launched upon a heroic vision of man's necessary suffering and fall. He gloried in it. It had spiritual value. The greater the seeming temporal disaster, the greater the spiritual fruit thereof. His lines ran with war imagery: burning tanks, shattered corpses, men choking with thirst in the desert. Recent horrors were being exorcised, and through them came this cry of faith.

It seemed that that Saturday night when he had cried, "I would rather die, die in the flesh to live in the spirit," he had not just been talking politics, nor with the Arab's sense of moral outrage, but already with some indication of the creative forces sparked in himself. Like any artist, whatever he discoursed on, it primarily reflected the state of his art.

Along with this burning note of passion, his verse reflected the mountain scene, the daily task that a man pursued until he was called to the testing moment. Patience. Diligence. The day well filled with reverence for the land and its gods. He had caught the age-old peasant feeling. He was identifying himself with the village.

When he said, "I may never return to Beirut," one could believe him, though one could also see that the words marked a phase of creation. Each morning he sat in his orchard, at the far end under a walnut tree, from where he could watch the work on his house, and there (wearing a *kuffieh*, the head cloth, and an old khaki shirt and pants) he wrote, drinking in sights and sounds which also came through in his imagery, and also, at last, made him companionable. If he had stayed in Beirut, I doubt that he would ever have spoken to me again. His silence had burned unproductively and with the side effect of hatred for the foreigner. Up here this passion was transmuted. He didn't talk much, but he was friendly at least. We both assisted, as laborers, with the house. I had dug half of his terraces for him. In any case, Leila had sent me as someone "able to ignore his moods." I suppose that she had wanted another eye kept on him. She came herself, in various family cars, for the day, to fuss, then returned to her apartment. He, temporarily, had moved right away from her.

She must have experienced this before. She was being very understanding.

We stopped by the house. Raoul did not speak, but he gazed with satisfaction. This was his little window on the world, with the near view of steep, tiled roofs and flat roofs and church belfries gleaming in the misty moonlight, and on every side the wall of mountains. A community into which, unexpectedly, he was inserting himself with quiet authority. As a poet, he was given status by all, more than because he was one of the Hadiris. His walk was changing, his facial expressions. The village elders sought his views, and he had been taken onto one of the committees forever settling irrigation disputes or a charge that a boundary marker had been moved or, as in this case, that an envious neighbor had tried to destroy crops in the night.

As we walked on, we passed above the terraces where this destruction was said to have occurred. With the harvest approaching, clansmen would sleep in brush shelters by their crops, and the village as a whole paid a nightwatchman; but these terraces had been unguarded. There was a round threshing floor nearby. One could not, in this light, see any destruction, though it was never, as another villager had explained, such an easily determined issue, and the aim of a *wasta* was conciliation, not judgment as such, but mutual concessions that would lead to happier life between clans. What a sensible approach! And what a shame that Arabs and Jews could not use the formula. At village level good sense prevailed.

Raoul was sought as "a man of silence." His present mood, unintentionally, was building him up as a village worthy.

It was hard to say whether he knew this.

He was so busy transmuting into verse.

The path up the hillside was steep, treacherous, and like a knife for the feet. He set the pace. It was still too dark to detect every stone, and I stumbled and cut my ankles and shins. He seemed to go up like a goat. Wet bushes struck one's face. The moon had gone, and the stars were fading, and the dawn was coming over the crest, but in this gully it was more thickly dark. A moment to halt, and I tried to arrange this by pointing to the old oak down a side track

near to a spring bubbling from the mountain, which was a
sacred place to the villagers. Christians all, they nonetheless
brought coins and scraps of clothing and candles to offer,
as a guard against illness or evil, to the water and to the
tree spirits, and to Adonis and Astarte, the old Canaanite
gods, though these latter two were also referred to as St.
George and Our Virgin Lady. In any case, why not pray to
them all? Vast, centralized religious systems don't satisfy all
men's needs.

I said as much to Raoul.

He nodded, and continued. He was actually often drawn
to that oak, but today he was simply climbing the hill.

The light was coming, the first sunlit glow. Immediately
one saw how hot it would be and saw the point of Raoul's
persistence. The stones, the jutting rock, the crevices into
which one's feet could neatly fall were suddenly and alarm-
ingly apparent. We were leaving the area of vegetation,
except for pines, juniper, thorn, and all kinds of wild plants:
mint and vetch, clematis, iris, and aubretia and arabis, and
dog-rose. We pressed on. The village was receding, becoming
a single housing unit among its terraced crops and orchards.
Smoke was rising. There was a little group of figures starting
in our wake. A church bell rang. Then a spur of the hill cut
that scene.

Ribbed rock and channels of scree. Raoul said that it was
the quick way up. For tourists there might be a roundabout
path. Even the flocks came this way. It was still cool, but my
throat was drying, and my limbs refused to work together,
stretching up and slithering back. After all, he was a city
aesthete who had seemed to spend half his day in bed. But
the essential Arab was coming through now, wiry and indifferent to discomfort, driven, it would seem, by demoniac
urges to reach the summit in one quick go.

Suddenly we had company. A man on a donkey. It was

Ghalib, a villager suitably named, for he was known for always coming off best in anything that he undertook. Now, on his ass, he'd be first up the hill. Over water rights, he kept improving his share. In the coffee house, in a devious way, he could usually show that he had first predicted what had now become the news. At cousin Farid's political meeting it was he who had slaughtered the opposition.

He was, in fact, a village *qabadāy*, though, so far as I knew, not a murderous one.

He had a gun with him. Was he after birds? No, he told us, he had sheep further up on the stretch of plateau overlooking the Biqa'. He had promised the gun to one of the Bedouin who had done him a good turn earlier. He grinned wickedly. He must be up to mischief.

He dressed with dash: boots, *shirwal*, clean lawn shirt and fancy waistcoat, and on his finger a ruby ring. On his head a *kuffieh*. He was a convincing brigand.

There had been a rumor of a new route for hashish down through here to the coastal cutters, but only a rumor. Ghalib would know.

Politically, he was the villager more than others who stood for renewed war against Israel. It was his style, possibly: bluff and truculence.

For the tone up here, largely reflecting the shock and ambivalence of the city, had, since we had had a chance to know it, moved through a curiously passive phase. There had been the gloomy reports to contend with, of purges and taxes and tightening the belt from one or another Arab country, and then of the new moderate line, with its confession that the West could not be disciplined, but had better be wooed by more discreet methods. The Arabs, in fact, had really lost; the truth was catastrophic; they had better think again.

The villagers, shaking their heads and staring, had absorbed this, and one of their reactions had been to ask, with some insistence, who was this giant who had felled the Arabs? Being Christian and up in the mountains, they had not needed to pretend it was America. It was Israel. And just what was Israel? The talking-about-Israel phase had occurred.

Eshkol should go to Cairo!—declared someone—Eshkol should study Arab psychology! Dayan should do this, Rabin that, as befitted men who had conquered in battle. Come, let the Jews live in peace! No, for they were trying to annex Jerusalem. Ah, but that was a talking point! No, dear brother, they would keep it forever. It formed a part of their expansionist blueprint. These sabras, these prickly pears. What would they do to the Arab countries? But admit they had not raped, as predicted. No, but hadn't they flattened Qalqilya and other hamlets just as they pleased? A hard people. With a fortress mentality. Those brother Arabs who were locked in Israel would never be more than helots for the Jews. The Israelis would keep all they had taken. A hard people. God would destroy them.

"You are an Israeli spy," one man called another.

"You would recognize them . . . you believe their propaganda . . . you think that we ought to join their State. . . ."

Blows had followed, and Israel as a topic had subsequently waned in popularity. "As we see," our friend the elder had commented, "when we don't define our enemy properly, we fall out among ourselves!"

Israel had returned to being simply the enemy.

And about that time the press had extolled the new armaments received from Russia.

Ghalib had been listened to a little more intently.

I told you, he had crowed—sitting in the line of chairs outside the elder's house, repeating his remarks from orchard to orchard, bumping along the paths on his donkey—I told you. And there is also China! That Texan Nero who lights his cigar from the ashes of each smoldering battle will very shortly be brought to justice. I shouldn't be surprised if it happens in a month!

Yes, this same Ghalib who was climbing with us now, contentedly letting his donkey kick loose stones back against our shoes. He had taken the lead. He was whacking his beast. If we meant to keep up, we should have to sweat.

Last week cousin Farid had appeared. Well, he had been more than once, with his son Augusto, the marriageable Casanova from São Paolo. But last week the visit had been solely in his capacity as a political firebrand. A huge evening rally had been organized. The Kataeb had not exactly sponsored it, nor had the Hadiri clan been pleased, for Farid Hadiri was unpredictable; but somehow through Ghalib and other workers (no doubt remunerated from the factory), and through his reputation as a speaker, a vast crowd had been drawn together—from the district, from other valleys of the Mountain, and by carload up from the city itself. People had been in the mood to listen, to know really what to think next. Farid could be counted on for fireworks. He must have cleared his speech with the army, but he could be counted on to say something more. He would leave Nassib to square that one for him. Hence, the Hadiri disapproval.

What an occasion! A moonlight gathering decked out by oil flares. It was as if all the wicks that burned nightly to keep the evil djinns at bay had been magnified a hundredfold. All the evil in the world would be banished by cousin Farid's shining countenance. He had appeared as the Christian knight in armor.

Another speaker first; a call for Arab unity; a call for the traditional measure of Lebanon. Brother Muslims, brother Christians, a free economy, a fence to sit on. . . .

Then Farid: "We stand at the crossroads!" Excitement,

concentration on the speaker. Raoul, who had consented to come along, gave me the rough translation later, but even at the time I could catch the spirit and the key words for America and Russia.

"We stand at the crossroads, O Christian brothers!" Farid knew who his audience were. "We stand there taking our decision . . . and what must we take our decision about? About Communism! And about freedom. About whether we go, like President Nasser, in overalls to unload armaments that will turn us into Russia's slaves, or whether, remembering who murdered the Czar, we say no to Podgorny, no to Brezhnev, no to Kosygin, and keep our Lebanon safe from this stealthy approach of the Bear. Do we want Beirut to become a naval base for the Russian fleet? Are we to accept their quartermastering? No, Christian brothers of the Lebanese Mountain. No, a thousand times no to Russia and to her aim of climbing upon our shoulders for a vantage point against the USA. Make no mistake! We are the puppets. The only concern of Russia is America. Arabs mean very little to the Moscovites. The aim of Communism is russification. Let us therefore declare ourselves for Christianity . . . for western democracy . . . and for an internationally neutralized Lebanon! Like Switzerland, let us stand aside!"

Roars of approval, but some dissension. And there, contrariwise, considering his views, Ghalib and his cronies had silenced the offenders. How to explain it, for Farid was not calling for any action against the Jews? (On the contrary, he was saying: "Let time decide this, for we have a Trojan Horse in that country . . . a quarter, soon half, of their population. With patience we shall take that country from within.") I think Ghalib, apart from the pay he was getting, backed the speaker because he always backed the most rambunctious cause at any given moment. And Farid made his pacifist call for an internationally neutralized Lebanon into a most aggressive idea. A cause. A challenge. Bang! And the crowd, especially those with that sort of chemistry, reacted to the pure excitement of the speech.

Such is the power of even local demagogues.

And no one since appeared to have questioned this Ghalib over his inconsistency.

His stock appeared to be daily rising.

Just now he was saying, as he scrambled ahead of us, his beast dropping dung in our faces, "Mark my words, O cousins, whether or not that Russian Bear be sincere, the Arab Hawk will strike again soon. Silently . . . out of the night . . . to victory!"

And with a tremendous clatter he whacked his beast up a short pebbly incline and away along a level path. Minutes, and he had gone from view.

Raoul laughed shortly and was silent. He was seeing politics as superficial.

Four hours after our departure, we reached the summit that was our objective. There were higher peaks still under snow, but from here we could see the Biqa' and Mount Hermon, and to the west the rising clouds of mist that signified the Mediterranean. At last Raoul allowed a rest.

He unpacked our food: minty sandwiches, dried figs, nuts, fresh fruit. A bottle of *araq*, which was his idea. We sat in the shade of a rock and rested. The sun was already noticeably hot. It was just after eight in the morning.

A child appeared, scampering round the rock. Seeing us, she stood very still. Raoul spoke soothingly in Arabic.

"They are herdsmen, coming from Syria. They have sheep and goats. She has been sent for brushwood. Why don't you give her your chocolate?"

I offered it, but she remained staring.

"Come," he said, after speaking again to her, "she will take us down to see her father. Have you cigarettes? These people are generous."

The child danced about on the rocks, not seeming to notice their cutting edges. We covered a hundred yards of rocks, as one might for shrimps on the sea shore, then slithered down scree to a protected wadi. Here the herdsmen had their tents. They were cooking a meal. There was a tinkling of bells. The child took us to a goatskin tent.

We were well received. The old man looked murderous, but his every gesture was thoughtful and refined. Fresh goat's milk was at once brought for us, and curds of cheese, bread, and figs. They had fruit that must have come from the coast. He might have been staring into our souls, so intently did he follow our eating. Then he and Raoul had a conversation.

"He asks," said Raoul, "if you are in flight from your country? Perhaps you do not like its laws?"

"I have a high regard for this country. And for all those of Arab people."

"You remind him of a Frenchman he met on Hermon. Why do you people leave your homes?"

"Is he not himself a wanderer? Is this not also of the nature of life?"

"He is very glad that we have come to see him." There were gracious nods. "His son has been brought and is at this moment sitting outside. I think—"

But the sound of the flute playing explained what the son had been sent for. Entertainment after food and conversation. This wild-looking herdsman in his rocky pastures had only one standard, that of a prince. It was true to tell him, as I did through Raoul, that to be received like this further answered his question: this was why it was good to be a traveler.

One can't have it, vicariously, in an armchair.

It is not one's own off the television screen.

Travelers are right to be individualists.

We departed, bearing a gift of fruit. They even had better cigarettes than mine. We scrambled back up the waterless wadi, regained our plateau, and halted again. A church bell was ringing. There were distant gun shots. Down a valley to the west, where a curve of road climbed a ridge, we could make out a cortège of eight cars following a hearse. A common sight in this countryside. Whole communities took the day off to chant and wail and to wave farewell. If the dead one was a child, they danced before the coffin. They were stricken, but they took it in the course of life. Christians or Muslims, they felt God's plan. Death was not a problem to these people.

It caused Raoul to recite a poem in Arabic. "I can't put it into English or French. It is a traditional lyric for such an occasion. May he rest in peace."

"You know," he went on, "people talk about change. About how we are a changing society. About how we must change into modern people, all presumably to be alike. But that's not for me. I cling to old fragments and residues and pockets of the past. And I hope that this country will do the same and confound all the modernizing experts. Let's keep our clan society; let's cling to our ways. You know, the truth is—but don't tell Leila—I think I shall stay all winter in the village. Be snowed up. It's a state of mind—yes, I recognize that—but it is what we need. To be cut off from the western world. You are uncaringly destroying values that with less pressure might be transplanted. At least, I have to look for this in my verse."

We began, without thinking, to descend toward the village. If we took it gently, we should be back by two. "Leila might come up again today." He was pretty guilty with regard to Leila.

But now, anyway, he was in a much better mood. The

climb, the summit, the return to the village; he was mapping out what he could live with. Much of the argument had ended in him.

We saw her under the carob tree about fifty yards above Raoul's house. She was gasping for breath, and her face was red. Her hair was disarrayed, and she was crying from the effort. But even as we called to her, she, not hearing, again lunged on, up the hill in our direction. "Leila, stop!" Raoul ordered. "Is she crazy, with a heart like that?" He rushed down and began skidding and caught at a tree to halt his fall. He landed almost at Leila's feet.

"What do you think you're doing? My beloved sister! Why couldn't you wait in the orchard? Did they tell you that we had gone to the summit?"

Scolded, she began to smile with pleasure. "I thought . . . a little exercise"—she panted—"I've brought a picnic . . . ready in the orchard . . . Nassib's man. . . ."

"Is he here?"

"No, gone back. Hoda's at her house. Do you mean . . . you have been up there?" She indicated the distant crest as though it were one of the mansions of heaven.

"I can't get over it." Raoul was nearly weeping. "Were you trying to follow our path?"

"I didn't get far," she temporized. Her devotion, her yearning, were so self-evident.

True enough, there was an ample repast waiting for us in Raoul's orchard. Austerity days with this family often ended in overeating. The wife of one of the masons at work had been guarding it against dogs or children, and now, as we approached, she added her small gift of almonds to our table. Her own children played in the shade, and of course Leila had been spoiling them. Though quite large children, they had not been weaned, nor toilet trained, and they kept making messes, but nobody seemed to think anything of it. Among the sweet smells and the misty views there were also children's faces and flies.

We drank several *araqs*, and all was well. There were vine leaves packed with meat and rice, a tray of *kibbeh*, salads, fruit. Leila had set the food on a table and arranged a wicker chair for each of us. We ate in style, as one ate at the apartment, taming the mountain view a little. Raoul was most solicitous for her, and she, peeping a little fearfully out of that wise, careworn face—that huge, aghast expression of hers, as I should always remember it from the week of the war— was beginning also to quiver with excitement. She had, she confessed, something to tell us. She was heaving with it suddenly. Her piece of news. . . .

Maurice was going to marry Yola!

Allâhu akbar! Raoul stared, then muttered something swift in Arabic. Then he smiled mysteriously, waiting to hear more.

The background to this announcement we all knew well, too well, Raoul had been saying each time that cousin Farid had turned up, touring the Mountain with his son Augusto and one or another of the girls in tow. For the commotion had started with Augusto. He was visiting Lebanon to select a wife from among his cousins preferably. And he was so good-looking, so vain, and so theatrically emotional that he had imagined he could take whom he pleased. Among men whose party talk was money, he had stood out as a galloping Lothario. Collectively, Les Jeunes Filles had swooned. Individually, they had been less sure. Leila had both encouraged and cautioned.

But it was Sheik Nassib who, when Yola was chosen, had said no, there were other plans for her. Farid had taken this refusal badly. For the other plans had not been disclosed. Yola had merely been told to stay at home. And she had

looked on while Augusto, unperturbed, had cavaliered Coco,
then Marie-Rose. Farid was nearly always of the party. He
doted on Augusto, and he was trying his best to persuade him
to settle down in Lebanon. These odd trios had kept gracing
the village, where Farid also had a property.

"So you see," elucidated Leila with excitement, "there was
probably an understanding all along. I don't think Maurice
could just be told to do it—"

"Ah," cried Raoul, "but I bet that he was! Christiane
packed off to Cairo, Robert silenced, the next election assured
—our Sheik is suddenly showing his power, left, right, and
center, and we all know why. The war has made it possible
for him. His political position is now impregnable. He speaks,
and he really enjoys it, from strength. Of course he told
Maurice to get married! And he told Yola that he'd stand
no nonsense. He couldn't endure a third child rebelling."

"Poor Christiane!" Leila sighed momentarily; then she began
to exult again in the news. It was a sort of compensation for
her. There would be so much to do in assisting Yola. "I am
really pleased about it," she continued. "An arranged match.
That is always best. Then one of the others will go to
Augusto. He's not a bad boy."

Raoul snorted.

"There will be so much to think of," she insisted.

They fell silent for a time, affectionately, but really worlds
apart now.

A figure in a beautiful *gumbaaz*—the tubular gown of
striped white silk—came through the orchard. Our friend the
elder. He, certainly, was pleased these days, for Sheik Nassib
had fulfilled all promises. Robert, undeniably, had toed the
line. Robert, they were saying (I hadn't seen him myself),
had been very perplexed since the end of the war. He had
given in and signed the paper promoting this elder's favorite
nephew; and afterward he had seemed to lose interest. He

had said that he was reconsidering his position and that he might leave the Government service. The Sheik, they were saying, had pulled no punches. Raoul declined to discuss it much. "They'll put Robert into an Embassy," he said.

One could record these facts. One had to think out just why the Sheik had become more powerful.

The Six Day War. The tilt in the balance between different interests in Lebanon. . . .

Oh, Raoul was useless nowadays to talk to!

The elder approached with an ingratiating bow. "*As-salâmu 'alaykum!*" His right hand touched his heart then his lips, then his forehead, as he bowed. He had to be pressed several times to be seated. He made propritiatory sighs and grunts like a sow while settling in, and he refused food. He had himself brought a small gift, a fragment of a painted Roman vase once dug up in his garden, which he was suggesting Raoul should bury in his walls before the reconstruction was completed. To be at one with the past. He hadn't seemed to notice that the fragment had exceptional beauty. Raoul thanked him and promised to comply.

Then the elder spoke of the village subjected to dangerous summer influences: the student volunteers who had arrived from France (a noble country, praise God, at this time!) to help with a stretch of road higher up, who invaded the village quiet in the evenings with their girls in miniskirts and slacks. This year there was a stereo club playing Greek *bouzouki* records. He was against it. With the Third World War almost certainly started (he still held to this view, and was not deceived by the "present lull following a battle"), wanton behavior might be singled out by angels settling accounts with men. In the ultimate scenes virtue and vice would be weighed upon the celestial scales. He was battling to keep the village pure.

Apropos of this, he felt it was time that the girl Hoda got married.

The real meat of his visit.

Leila, sharpened and switching to Arabic, mounted a defense. Gone in a flash the sleepy Aunty-from-Egypt with her passive and dilapidated look. She was suddenly a determined lady of position putting this rural sage in his place. Hoda, she apparently said, was hers until she determined otherwise. In any case the maid was needed now with all these Hadiris getting married.

The elder pricked up his ears but was silent, conscious of where he should not trespass.

Very shortly afterward, he left us.

"Bravo," muttered Raoul, for Leila was still fuming, "but I hope that he doesn't put the evil eye on me. I, after all, have to keep in with him. With all these village elders now."

"Pff, Nassib has him in his pocket!" She would not give ground over Hoda. "I shall bring him a present next time I come here."

"Yes, please do that. I am glad you let fly. It gives you such a good color, sister."

Leila gradually became herself again.

We sat through the afternoon heat, talking. The light bounced off the hills. It quivered as though to burn the village. Only in the orchard did it seem subdued. The men worked steadily on the house, though elsewhere work looked suspended until the twilight cool returned. A motorcycle snorted away; a service-taxi brought some nuns; a donkey brayed. Cicadas ticked unceasingly very close to us. We sat through the heat, drinking fresh lemonade, and as Raoul recounted stories from the village, old stories that showed its way of thinking, Leila too began to take an interest, and she said, "Would you be lonely here if I left you for a month or so, Raoul? With these village things to think about?"

"Why, Leila?" He looked surprised.

"Nassib thinks I should go to America since Charlie can't come here. Nassib is offering to take me in September when he also has to go there. I was afraid to ask you!" She really had been, so tied was she to his dependence on her.

It was impossible to fathom his expression.

Uncertainly he said, "Yes. Go."

She smiled gratefully, then in a different way. She no doubt deeply understood him.

As usual, I drove her back from the village, at least as far as the Sheik's villa, where someone else would ferry her to town. Tonight, however, I was conducting her all the way down to Beirut. Raoul waved us away as usual, though not quite so offhandedly as sometimes.

It was twilight. That had brought out the cars.

The Sheik's mountain villa, hub of his power during the summer months, had a surface air of genial frivolity. It danced with light in the velvet evening—light for the tennis court and the pool, for the card games, for the cocktail dresses worn before the nighttime round of drinks and dinners and hilltop cabarets split its members into various groups to add their cars to the crowd on the road. In the twilight the roads were truly pastoral, cars resembling fat-tailed sheep or long-horned cattle moving in droves toward some necessary watering place. By the villa door there was nowhere to park except alongside Maurice's car, driven onto a flower bed. There was a guard on duty. One walked through the house, welcome to any part of the assembly. Friends, relations mostly, appeared, disappeared, came around again in a seemingly endless perambulation from one hill villa to another. "Lulu? Georges? Yes, they were here. We were talking." But it might have been somewhere else and yesterday. They were enjoying themselves in a ceaseless present.

The Sheik was at cards in the first, long room. There were genial, cigar-throated protests and quips and a call for more whiskey. A male servant attended the players. Across the courtyard, on the upper level, his wife and mother were seated on the balcony, flanked by a tittering group of girls. They were eagerly examining the first photographs taken of Yola and Maurice together. Neither of these two were present. What struck one about the likeness of Maurice was how his feline gifts came through, compounded with his streak of cruelty, while beside him Yola looked demure, a handmaid, a milkmaid of love, such as she never looked in life. Photographic play. The group was amused and was complimenting Sarkoubian, who, in the background, wisp-like as ever, seemed promoted above his usual station at Leila's. Perhaps these ladies had only just discovered what a useful person he was.

In the courtyard by the fountain there was another nucleus, centered on a sister-in-law of the Sheik, an artist who lived and painted in Paris, a formidably fine-featured woman, very popular with Les Jeunes Filles because she had suffered in love and was happy to talk about it and, also, about her hundreds of conquests. She came over here each summer, and she was a center of anarchy and anti-religion; but so tolerant was the villa mood that she was a favorite even with Madame Hadiri. The two sisters went to church together. Then this one filled the courtyard with her paintings, propped up as in a pavement show. In the early hours the servants stacked them. During the day she painted and talked and teased the Sheik (she was the only one who dared) and incited the girls to follow her lead. "Get out! Get away! Don't let money destroy you." She rattled her wrists loaded with jewelry. "Love is the third dimension of life. Why are you Orientals ashamed of it?" Leila said that the girls, un-known to her, had tape-recorded her dissertations and wanted to sell them to a cabaret. Of course they never would.

I was looking for Lulu, but I couldn't find her. By the

swimming pool I found Maurice and Yola together with Sami Hadiri and his wife. Yola did resemble the photograph, sweet and subdued, and the way she served a drink was right outside her tomboy style. One had to see her as replacing Christiane. She was more the answer for a rising magnate who one day, in politics also, might contend for the leading post; she was so clearly the family choice, the right consort for the probable winner. One might think the family rugged over this, but they were basically an enterprise; and Christiane just wasn't an asset, couldn't be one until much later when, having led her irregular life elsewhere, she could return like this artist aunt of hers and fill out the frivolity of summer.

Normal family life, like business-politics, was a serious, highly conformist affair.

Secretly, of course, one could prefer Christiane.

As soon as I could get Maurice alone, and all the compliments had been said, I sought his views on the political outlook. He was the one who talked most freely, his talent for success emboldening him to state his preference and to crystal gaze. At first now he was a bit more cautious, having become engaged and so on, but he was vain with his views, and he was really anxious to see a workable peace in the area.

"The Arab spokesmen go hither and thither—it's amazing how they circulate—we wait on their words and are mesmerized! Are the onlookers—Israel, Russia, America—deceived by this show of Arab unity? We wait on a chain of summit conferences, knowing already that each will concede a little more to world opinion! Of course our leaders will assure one another that they are working hard upon the West: neutralizing, one by one, countries that have supported Israel. Time, they will claim, favors them (either for peace or for war), so concede a little, be Arab, be clever. One can see their adroit policies unfolding."

"Surely, though, as Farid claimed—you must have heard

of what he said at the rally—there is a Trojan Horse within Israel?"

"Oh yes, with various solutions. The Israelis are not friends, after all. They are administrators, like all the world. There, for instance"—he was becoming more involved—"I should think it cleverer to shape our policies to influence their younger generation than to act as if they were unimpressionable. I think it would pay us a dividend. Those *sabras* will pay a good price to be told that they are accepted into the area. Israel is a fact. We should talk to her directly—as, behind the scenes, I am told that we do—rather than so easily mortgage our interest to the Big Power on either side. . . ."

He paused, then continued, "We need open frontiers, trade, and technological alliance. We are a few plains and hills by a sea. Geographically, we are one unit. I say, make peace with Israel, because I am not afraid of the outcome. As a Lebanese I can hold my own. As a Christian, as an Arab, whatever you call me, I am not afraid of these new neighbors. Rather, once the frontiers are down, I think they should be afraid of me!

The alternative: a hundred years of dependency, semi-dependency, possibly on Russia, with as much voice and economic advance as the Uzbekis and those kinds of Asians. Egypt is really a baneful influence. I hope the Palestinians, who hold the key, will speak up for themselves in time."

"You are an optimist then? The Middle East can be saved?"

"Alas, no, I can't say that. Emotion, not reason, rules the Arab. In fact, one horrifying possibility is that this area will see the use of nuclear arms on a limited scale, a kind of test case to warn the world to put such weapons away forever. A general war wouldn't follow from it. A test case is a certainty somewhere. Vietnam has become too risky. We may be chosen as guinea pigs."

"Chosen? That's an ugly idea."

"And the world in which we live? Such things are done in the name of the earthly paradise to follow!"

"Meanwhile, you seem happier about Lebanon."

"Of course. We shall all be more Lebanese." He stressed the "all." He was not playing politics. He said soberly, "Hamid is consenting to talk business with me again. As we have to. It is trade, and now light industry, that must come first for Lebanon. And don't fear: we shan't exclude the majority from the new wealth that arises. That kind of situation is finished."

One hoped that it was; and it might be for him, planning a profit from any situation, though one supposed that families such as the Hadiris or the Zoghals or a few score others would for several decades to come garner the first fruits of the land. They would keep the sumptuous villas, the big cars, the expense accounts. Fun on such a scale was only for a few. Only a few could be at the top.

Even in a rapidly changing world, Lebanon would change gradually.

I asked him, "Have you seen Lulu?"

He made an impolite noise. "That Brazilian freak, failing with my sister, has now attached himself to Lulu."

"Augusto?"

"The same. They are out with cousin Farid. Lulu, I am sorry to hazard, will take him. In São Paolo she will be safe from her mother."

"Oh." The way of all young girls. Sooner or later they had to make the gamble. Les Jeunes Filles were tumbling fast.

As Leila said when we were in the car again, "The others are going to be so restless. I shall be so busy for the next two years." She enclosed herself within that time scale, laughing and sighing, and filling any void with warm memories of her own young days. She looked pretty exhausted, however. This latest war shock, with Raoul's withdrawal, had undermined her tenuous security.

Before leaving the villa I had a word with the Sheik. His card game finished, he was sitting with his mother. He was dressed in blue linen trousers, canvas shoes, a white chunky sweater; and he drew attention to this as the gear he had worn while refereeing the tennis. "*Je suis en déshabille*. I am on holiday. Look! I am enjoying the simple mountain pleasures." Behind his bushy eyes lurked amusement. Of course, why not? He was sitting pretty.

Though, his mountain routine still took him to his office, six days a week, at seven a.m. He was back for lunch and a short siesta. It was after that the simple pleasures commenced. Next week, together with these ladies and Yola, he was off to Zurich, a twice-yearly visit, and from there he was flying on to London. Badri would run the setup here. Though, thanks to the speeding up that the war had brought to every department of life, it was Badri's son, the agile Maurice, who was emerging as the heir-apparent. With Robert and Sami disqualified, and the youngest son Joseph only twelve, the speed of events, the Maronite time scale, demanded a new young leader in the wings, to be groomed now for a decade hence. Elie and Georges were too retiring. Christiane was a girl, as also was Amale. Only Maurice had all the requirements, and to make this doubly clear to the world, he was being matched with the nubile Yola. First cousins. The Sheik's creatures. It was a sure bet that in ten years time Maurice would be a leading politician.

For the moment the simple mountain pleasures.

The Sheik had only jokes to tell one.

These Maronites were sitting pretty. From here the borders of Greater Lebanon had never looked so secure as now. The Muslims living within those borders would lose their last doubts about it and opt to become just Lebanese. Nineteen fifty-eight had been capped by this war. Again the army had armed the Constitution; Lebanon had come to stay. The Maronites, in 1970, could go all out for a strong

President, no longer to be seen as a communal bias, but as meaning the choice of a free economy rather than any Socialist solution or a solution leaning in that direction. Robert and Hamid could still campaign for their social welfare ideas, but ultimately the machinery embodying their ideas would be determined by men like Maurice.

A swing back to the right?

Is the left so progressive in the speed of creating wealth and bounty?

Lebanon stands (as does Japan; why always mention America?) for the progressive right-hand side. Its case is still as good as the others in this messy century we are living through.

We said goodnight to the Sheik and his family. Leila was still lisping with gossip. Christiane was not, as all had supposed, working for Hamid's paper in Egypt, but doing market research for the Sheik. Too unnerved by what had been happening, she had thrown herself back on her father. He had understood; he had provided this work. She could live in Egypt, where she liked the regime. It seemed, then, that even under a dictator the Hadiris could get back into Cairo! Leila was amused, though sad, too. It started all that old nostalgia.

As we drove down, our silences lengthened. She gossiped so long as we were among the lights and all the jazz of the mountain villages converted into summer main streets. She talked about the Debutantes' Ball, about the elopement that was saving marriage expenses for a particularly rich and stingy family, and about how a first and a second wife had ganged up against the husband—the usual small talk, passed from the girls. And she had a convent story, from the older generation. And because I should soon be leaving for England, she remembered her own sole visit there and how green and winding were the lanes.

Then we came upon an accident, the still smoking shell of two cars and their occupants. Police headlights blazoned the scene, accident assessors were measuring and arguing. The ambulance had already departed. There was delay and chaos among the rest of the traffic, people slowing to stare and point, others passing at every angle, impatient or possibly even whetted to add their own disaster. She gasped. She gave me conflicting advice. Her eyes dilated as we slid along the verge, with the precipice falling to the plain beneath us, in the final swing past the obstruction. "Oh, you must never do that again. I can't see! How can you see where the edge is? Everyone uses their lights against us!"

It was true. Descending the hill to Beirut was like facing the beams of interrogators sweating out one's nerves in a cellar. Even the steamy temperature rise added to this picture of torture. It was hit-or-miss at one or two moments. I was no happier than she.

Hoda, a silent bundle at the back, kept drawing in her breath sharply.

We made it. I said good night quickly and strolled down to the waterfront.

One could stand on the rocks—it was cool and dark—with fingers of mist close to the water, coiling just above the reflections cast by a window higher up, which itself caught the lights of the city. Beirut image, softly transplanted, healed of its stress for good and evil, reflecting only, on the soft night water, its presence, its uniqueness in the world.

One had to put the stress back in, though.

The human thing.

Them.

Us.

The Author

JOHN SYKES' twelve previous books have a cosmopolitan range. The English writer has produced travel books about Japan and Peru, and in 1965 he had a notable success with *Caique: a Portrait of Greek Islanders*. The latest of his seven novels, *The Couple* (1966), had contemporary Poland for a setting, and its predecessor, *The Heat of Summer*, had as a background the French Mediterranean coast. World War II found him in service not only in Finland but also in the Middle East and Greece. Besides working on his eighth novel, he is now involved in a study of present-day Egypt. For this his headquarters is Cairo, a city that must be ranked by the West today as one of the most unknown on earth.